THE SAFFRON ROBE

High in the rarefied air of the Himalayas, stands the great lamasery of Potala and here, as a young boy, Lobsang Rampa came to study the teachings of the Lord Buddha.

Through the eyes of this young acolyte we learn of the life of Prince Gautama and his discovery of the Middle Way, the Four Noble Truths and the State of Nirvana.

Those who have read of Lobsang Rampa's experiences in the lamaseries of Tibet, will be touched by this personal story of the transition of a daring and sometimes disobedient youth into a serious, deep-thinking young man possessing quite exceptional sensory abilities.

THE SAFFRON ROBE
by Lobsang Rampa

BANTAM BOOKS
· TORONTO · NEW YORK · LONDON ·
A NATIONAL GENERAL COMPANY

THE SAFFRON ROBE
*A Bantam Book / published by
arrangement with author*

PRINTING HISTORY
Corgi Books edition published February 1966
2nd printing .... April 1967   3rd printing ... September 1968
4th printing .... November 1969
Bantam edition published June 1970
2nd printing ..... February 1973

*Bantam Books are published by Bantam Books, Inc., a National
General company. Its trade-mark, consisting of the words "Bantam
Books" and the portrayal of a bantam, is registered in the United
States Patent Office and in other countries. Marca Registrada.
Bantam Books, Inc., 666 Fifth Avenue, New York, N.Y. 10019.*

PRINTED IN THE UNITED STATES OF AMERICA

To
Sheelagh M. Rouse
Honi soit que mal y pense—
Gaudet tentamine virtus

THE SAFFRON ROBE

CHAPTER ONE

STRANGE shadows rippled before my uncaring gaze, undulating across my vision like colorful phantoms from some remote, pleasant world. The sun-dappled water lay tranquil inches from my face.

Gently I inserted my arm below the surface, watching the lazy little waves which the motion caused. Squint-eyed I peered into the depths below. Yes, that big old stone, that is where he lived—and he was coming out to greet me! Idly I let my fingers trail along the sides of the now-motionless fish, motionless save for the easy movement of the fins as he "kept station" by my fingers.

He and I were old friends; often I would come and drop food into the water for him before caressing his body. We had the complete understanding which comes only to those who have no fear of each other. At that time I did not even know that fish were edible! Buddhists do not take life or inflict suffering on others.

I took a deep breath and pushed my face below the surface, anxious to peer more closely into another world. Here I felt like a god gazing down at a very different form of life. Tall fronds waved faintly in some unseen current; sturdy water-growths stood erect like the giant trees of some forest. A sandy streak meandered along like a mindless serpent, and was fringed with a pale green plant looking for all the world like a well-kept lawn.

Tiny little fish, multicolored and with big heads, flashed and darted among the plants in their continual search for food and fun. A huge water-snail laboriously lowered itself down the side of a great grey rock so that it could do its task of cleaning the sand.

But my lungs were bursting; the hot noonday sun was scorching the back of my neck, and the rough stones of the foreshore were digging into my flesh. With a last look around, I rose to my knees and thankfully breathed deep of the scented air. Here, in MY world, things were very different from the placid world which I had been studying. Here there was bustle, turmoil, and much scurrying about. Staggering a little from a healing wound in my left leg, I stood and rested with my back against a favorite old tree and looked about me.

The Norbu Linga was a blaze of color, the vivid green of the willows, the scarlet and gold of the Island Temple, and the deep, deep blue of the sky emphasized by the pure white of the fleecy clouds which came racing over the mountains from India. The calm waters of the lake reflected and exaggerated the colors and lent an air of unreality when a vagrant breeze roiled the water and caused the picture to sway and blur. All here was peaceful, quiet, yet just beyond the wall, as I could see, conditions were very different.

Russet-robed monks strode about carrying piles of clothes to be washed. Others squatted by the side of the sparkling stream and twisted and turned the clothes so that they should be well soaked. Shaven heads gleamed in the sunlight and, as the day progressed, gradually became sunburned. Small acolytes, newly joined to the lamasery, leaped about in a frenzy of excitement as they pounded their robes with big smooth stones that they should look older, more worn, and so give the impression that the wearer had been an acolyte longer!

Occasionally the sun would reflect bright shafts of light on the golden robes of some august lama journeying between the Potala and the Pargo Kaling. Most of them were men of staid appearance, men who had grown old in Temple service. Others, a very few, were young men indeed, some of them being Recognized

Incarnations, while others had progressed and advanced on their own merit.

Striding about, looking very alert and fierce, were the Proctors, large men from the Province of Kham, men charged with the task of maintaining discipline. Erect and bulky, they carried huge staves as a sign of their office. No intellectuals, these, but men of brawn and integrity and chosen for that alone. One came close and glowered inquiringly at me. Belatedly recognizing me he strode off in search for offenders worthy of his attention.

Behind me the towering bulk of the Potala—"the Home of the God"—soared skywards, one of the most glorious works of Man. The multi-hued rock glowed gently and sent vari-hued reflections skittering across the placid waters. By a trick of the shifting light, the carved and colored figures at the base seemed imbued with life, causing them to sway and move like a group of people in animated discussion. Great shafts of yellow light, reflected from the Golden Tombs on the Potala roof, sped off and formed vivid splashes on the darker mountain recesses.

A sudden "thunk" and the creak of bending wood caused me to turn to this new source of attraction. An ancient bird, grey and moulting, older than the oldest acolyte, had alighted on the tree behind me. Eyeing me with remarkably beady eyes, it said "cruaak!" and suddenly shuffled so that its back was toward me. It stretched to full length and violently flapped its wings while expelling an unwanted "gift" in my direction with astonishing force and precision. Only by a desperate jump aside did I escape being a target. The bird shuffled around to face me again and said "cruaak! cruaak!" before dismissing me from its attention in favor of the greater interest elsewhere.

On the gentle breeze came the first faint sounds of an approaching group of traders from India. The lowing of yaks as they protested at their drovers' attempts to hurry them. The asthmatic creak and wheeze of old dry leather-harness, the plod and shuffle of many feet and the musical tinkle of small pebbles being jostled aside by the caravan. Soon I could see the lumbering beasts, piled high with exotic bundles. Great horns tossing above shaggy eyebrows, the rise and fall as the huge animals stumped along with their slow, untiring gait. The traders, some with turbans, some with old fur hats, others with battered felt headgear.

"Alms, alms for the love of God," cried the beggars. "Ah!" they shouted as the traders moved on unfeelingly, "Your mother is a cow who mated with a boar, your seed is the seed of Sheitan, your sisters are sold in the market place!"

Strange odors came to twitch my nostrils, making me draw in a deep breath—and then sneeze heartily. Scents from the heart of India, bricks of tea from China, ancient dust being shaken from the yak-borne bales, all were wafted my way. Into the distance faded the sound of the yak bells, the loud talk of the traders, and the imprecations of the beggars. Soon the ladies of Lhasa would have wealthy callers at their doors. Soon the shopkeepers would be haggling over prices demanded by the traders; raised eyebrows and higher-raised voices at the inexplicably increased prices. Soon I would have to be going back to the Potala.

My attention wandered. Idly I watched the monks at their ablutions, two of them ready to come to blows over the threat of thrown water from one. Rapidly the Proctors moved in, a flurry of motion, and two chastened monks were marched off, each in the iron grip of "Guardians of the Peace."

But what was that? I let my gaze search the bushes. Two tiny glittering eyes looked anxiously at me from near-ground level. Two small grey ears were inclined intently in my direction. A minute body was crouched ready to rush should I make a false move. A little grey mouse was pondering the possibility of passing between me and the lake on its way home. As I looked, he darted forward, all the time keeping his gaze on me. His care was misplaced; not looking where he was going, he charged headlong into a fallen branch and—with a shrill squeak of terror—leaped a foot in the air.

4

He jumped badly, jumped too far to the side. As he came down he missed his footing and fell into the lake. The poor mite was making no headway and was in danger of being seized by a fish, when I stepped knee-deep into the water and scooped him up.

Carefully drying him with the end of my robe, I waded back to the shore and placed the shivering little bundle on the ground. Just a faint blur—and he vanished down the little burrow, no doubt thankful for his escape. Above me the ancient bird uttered a "cruaak!" of derision, and creaked laboriously into the air, flapping noisily in the direction of Lhasa.

In the direction of Lhasa? That reminded me, I should be going in the direction of the Potala! Over the Norbu Linga wall monks were stooping, examining the washing drying on the ground. Everything had to be carefully scrutinized before it could be picked up; Little Brother Beetle may be strolling across the clothing; and to roll up the garments would be to crush Little Brother—an act to make a Buddhist priest shudder and turn pale.

Perhaps a little worm had taken shelter from the sun beneath a high lama's laundry, then little worm must be removed to safety so that his destiny may not be altered by Man. All over the ground monks were stooping, peering, and gasping with relief as one little creature after another was safely delivered from certain death.

Gradually the piles of washing grew as everything was heaped ready to be taken into the Potala. Small acolytes staggered along under newly-washed burdens; some could not see over that which they were carrying. Then would come a sudden exclamation as a little fellow tripped and sent all the clothes flying to the dusty ground or even to the mud of the river bank.

From high on the roof came the throb and boom of the conches and the blare of the great trumpets. Sounds which echoed and re-echoed from the distant mountains so that at times, when conditions were right, vibrations pulsed about one and beat at one's chest for minutes. Then, suddenly, all would be still, so quiet that one could hear one's own heartbeat.

I left the shade of the friendly tree and made my halting way through a gap in the hedge. My legs were shaky; some time previously I had sustained a grave burn to my left leg—it did not heal well—and then had two legs broken when a great gust of wind had lifted me from the Potala roof and thrown me down the mountain side. So I limped, and for a short time was exempt from doing my share of household duties. My joy at that was offset by having to study more "that the debt may be set straight" as I was informed. Today—washday—I had been free to wander and rest in the Norbu Linga.

Not for me a return by way of the main entrance, with all the high lamas and abbots treading on one's heels. Not for me the hard, hard steps where I used to count "ninety-eight, ninety-nine, one hundred, one hundred and one. . . ." I stood by the side of the road while lamas, monks, and pilgrims passed by. Then there was a lull and I limped across the road and ducked into the bushes. Pulling myself along the precipitous mountain side, I made my ascending way above the Village of Shö and joined the side path between the Courts of Justice and the Potala.

The way was rugged, but beautiful with its profusion of small rock plants. The air was cooling, and my battered legs were beginning to ache intolerably. I gathered my tattered old robe about me and sat on a convenient rock so that I might regain my strength and my wind. Over in the direction of Lhasa I could see little sparkling fires—the traders were camping in the open, as Indians often did, rather than stay at one of the hostelries. Farther to the right I could see the shining river as it left on its immense journey all the way to the Bay of Bengal.

"Ur-rorr, ur-rorr!" said a deep bass voice, and a hard furry head butted me on the knees. "Ur-rorr, ur-ror!" I answered amiably. A blur of movement and a big black cat stood on my legs and pushed his face

6

into mine. "Honorable Puss Puss!" I said through thick fur. "You are choking me with your attentions." Gently I put my hands on his shoulders and moved him back a little so that I could look at him. Big blue eyes, slightly crossed, stared back at me. His teeth were as white as the clouds above and his widespread ears were alert to the slightest sound.

Honorable Puss Puss was an old and valued friend. Often we snuggled together beneath some sheltering bush and talked to each other of our fears, our disappointments, and all the hardships of our hard, hard life. Now he was showing his affection by "knitting" on me, opening and closing his big paws, while his purrs roared louder and louder. For a time we sat together, and then, together, we decided it was time to move.

As I toiled ever upward, stumbling from the pain in my damaged legs, Honorable Puss Puss raced ahead, tail stiffly erect. He would dive into some undergrowth and then, as I drew level, would spring out and cling playfully to my flapping robe. "Now! Now!" I exclaimed on one such occasion. "This is no way for the leader of the Cat Jewel Guard to behave." In reply, he laid his ears back and rushed up the front of my robe and, reaching my shoulder, jumped sideways into a bush.

It amused me to see our cats. We used them as guards, for a properly trained Siamese cat is fiercer than any dog. They would rest, apparently asleep, by the side of the Sacred Objects. If pilgrims attempted to touch or steal, then these cats—always in pairs—would seize him and hold him by menacing his throat. They were FIERCE, yet I could do anything with them and, being telepathic, we could converse without difficulty.

I reached the side entrance. Honorable Puss Puss was already there, energetically tearing great splinters off a wooden post by the side of the door. As I lifted the latch he pushed the door open with his strong head and vanished into the smoky gloom. I followed much more slowly.

This was my temporary home. My leg injuries were

7

such that I had been sent from Chakpori to the Potala. Now, as I entered the corridor, the familiar odors SMELT "home." The ever-present aroma of incense, the different perfumes according to the time and purpose for which it was being burned. The sour, rancid, and "stinging" smell from the yak-butter which we used in our lamps, for heating small articles such as kettles, and which we used for sculpture during the colder days. The "memory lingered on." No matter how hard we scrubbed (and we did not scrub too hard!) the scent was always there, permeating everything. A less pleasant smell was that of yak dung which, dried, was used for heating the rooms of the aged and infirm. But now I stumbled on, moving down the corridor past the flickering butter lamps which made the gloomy corridors gloomier still.

Another "perfume" was always present in all lamaseries, a "perfume" so familiar that one did not notice it unless hunger had sharpened one's perceptions. Tsampa! The smell of roasted barley, the smell of Chinese brick tea, the smell of hot butter. Mix them and the result is the inevitable, the eternal, tsampa. Some Tibetans have never tasted any other food than tsampa; they are born to the taste of it, and it is the last food they taste. It is food, drink, and consolation. It provides sustenance during the hardest manual labor; it provides food for the brain. But, it has ever been my belief, it starves sexual interest and so Tibet has no difficulty in being a celibate state, a land of monks, and with a falling birth-rate.

Hunger had sharpened MY perceptions, and so I was able to appreciate the aroma of roasted barley, hot butter, and Chinese brick tea! I walked wearily down the corridor and turned left when the scent was strongest. Here, at the great copper cauldrons, monk-cooks were ladling roasted and ground barley into bubbling tea. One hacked off several pounds of yak butter and tossed it in, another upended a leather sack of salt which had been brought by tribesmen from the Highland Lakes. A fourth monk, with a ten-foot paddle,

8

was stirring and swirling everything together. The cauldron bubbled and foamed and bits of twigs from the brick tea rose to the surface, to be swept off by the monk with the paddle.

The burning yak dung beneath the cauldron gave off an acrid stench and clouds and clouds of black soot. The whole place was coated, and the black, sweat-streaked faces of the monk-cooks could have been those of entities from some deep hell. Often the monk with the paddle would scrape floating butter from the cauldron and toss it on the fire. There would be a sizzle, a flare of flame, and a new stink!

"Ah, Lobsang!" yelled a monk above the clatter and clamor. "Come for food again, eh? Help yourself, boy, help yourself!" I took from inside my robe the little leather bag in which we monks kept a day's supply of barley. Shaking the dust out, I filled it to capacity with freshly roasted, freshly ground barley. From the front of my robe I drew my bowl and looked at it carefully. It WAS a bit grubby, a bit "caked." From the big bin against the far wall I took a handful of very fine sand and thoroughly scoured my bowl. It helped clean my hands as well! At last I was satisfied with its state. But another thing had to be done; my tea bag was empty, or rather, all it now contained was the small sticks, bits of sand, and other rubbish always found in the tea. This time I turned the bag inside out and picked free the debris. Returning the bag to its correct state, I took a hammer and knocked a suitable lump off the nearest brick of tea.

Now it was MY turn; once again I took my bowl—my newly cleaned bowl—and held it out. A monk took a ladle and slapped my bowl brimming full of tsampa. Thankfully I retired to a corner, sat on a sack, and ate my fill. As I ate, I looked about me. The kitchen was full of the usual hangers-on, idle men who lounged about gossiping, telling the latest scandal, adding a bit to rumors just heard. "Yes, Lama Tenching is going to the Rose Fence. 'Tis said he had a quarrel with the Lord Abbot. My friend heard it all he says. . . ."

People have many strange notions about lamaseries

or monasteries. It is often thought that monks spend the whole day in prayer, contemplation, or meditation— "looking good and saying only good things." A lamasery is a place where, officially, men of religious intent congregate for the purpose of worship and contemplation that the Spirit may be purified. Officially! Unofficially, a robe does not make a monk. In a community of several thousand there must be those who deal with household duties and repair and maintenance of the fabric. Others look after accounts, police the lower classes, teach, preach. . . . Enough! A lamasery may be a large town with an exclusively male population. The workers will be the lowest class of monks and will have no interest in the "religious" aspect of the life, paying only lip service to it. Some monks have never been in a Temple except to clean the floor!

A large lamasery will have a place of worship, schools, infirmary, stores, kitchens, hostels, prisons, and almost everything that would be found in a "lay" town. The main difference is that in a lamasery everyone, everything, is male and—on the surface— everyone is devoted to "religious instruction and action." Lamaseries have their earnest workers, and their well-meaning, bumbling "drones." The larger lamaseries are cities, or towns, with many buildings and parks spread over a wide area, sometimes the whole community is encircled by a high wall. Other lamaseries are small, possessing only a hundred monks and all housed in one building. In some remote areas, a very small lamasery may have no more than ten members. So, they range from ten to ten thousand, the tall and the short, the fat and the thin, the good and the bad, the lazy and the energetic. The same as in some outside community, no worse, and often not much better, except that Lamaistic DISCIPLINE may be almost military—it all depends on the abbot in charge. He may be a kind, considerate man, or he may be a tyrant.

I stifled a yawn and wandered out into the corridor. A rustling in one of the store alcoves drew my attention; I was in time to see a black tail vanish between leather sacks of grain. The cats were "guarding" the grain and at the same time catching their (mouse) supper. On top of one sack I saw a contented-looking cat cleaning his whiskers and fairly SMILING with satisfaction.

The trumpets sounded, reverberating through the echoing corridors, and sounding again. I turned and made my way to the Inner Temple to the sound of many shuffling sandals and the slap of bare feet.

Within, there was the deepening gloom of early evening, with the purple shadows stealing across the floor and limning the columns with ebony. The sides of the windows were edged with gold as the sun's fingers reached out and gave a last gentle caress to our home. Swirling clouds of incense drifted along and, when pierced by a shaft of sunlight, showed to be a myriad dust-motes of living colors almost endowed with life.

Monks and lamas, and humble acolytes, filed in and took their places upon the floor, each adding his own splash of color to be reflected upon the vibrant air. The gold robes of the Potala lamas, the saffron and red of others, the dark brown of monks, and the sun-bleached garments of those who habitually worked outside. All sat in lines in the approved position. I— because my severe leg injuries prevented me from sitting as prescribed—was relegated to a back position where I was hidden by a smoke-wreathed column so that I should not "destroy the pattern."

I looked about me, seeing all the boys, the men, and very old sages who were attending to their devotions each according to his understanding. I thought of my mother, the mother who had not even said "good-by" to me when I had left home—how long ago that seemed!—to enter the Chakpori Lamasery. Men, all men. I knew only about men. What were WOMEN like? I knew that in some parts of Tibet, there were monasteries where monks and nuns lived together, married, and raised their families.

The incense swirled on, the service droned on, and the dusk deepened into darkness barely relieved by the flickering butter lamps and the softly glowing incense. Men! WAS it right for men to live alone, to have no association with women? What were women like, anyhow, did they think the same as we? As far as I knew they chattered only about fashion, hair style, and silly things like that. They looked awful frights, too, with all the stuff they put on their faces.

The service ended, and I got up painfully on shaky legs and stood with my back to the column so that I would not be toppled over in the first rush. Finally, I moved into the corridor and made my way to the dormitory.

A chill wind was blowing through the open windows, blowing straight down from the Himalayas. The stars were shining bright and cold in the clear night air. From a window below me a quavering voice was reciting:

> Now this is the Noble Truth as to the origin of suffering. It is the craving thirst that causes the renewal of becomings. . . .

Tomorrow, I reminded myself, and for perhaps a few days after, we were going to have special lectures on Buddhism from one of the great Indian Teachers. Our Buddhism—Lamaism—had departed from the strict orthodox lines of Indian Buddhism in much the same way as the Christian belief had various forms such as Quaker and Catholic. Now, though, the night hours were far advanced, and I turned away from the frosty window.

About me acolytes were sleeping. Some snoring, a few tossed restlessly as they thought, maybe, of "home" as I had so recently been thinking. A few very hardy souls were trying to practice the "correct" Lamaistic sleeping posture—sleeping upright in the Lotus position. We had no beds, of course, nor mattresses. The floor was our table and our bed.

I took off my robe, shivering naked in the chill night air, and then wrapped myself in the blanket which all Tibetan monks carry as a roll over one shoulder and caught at the waist. Cautiously lowering myself to the floor in case my treacherous legs betrayed me, I bundled my robe beneath my head as a pillow and dropped off to sleep.

CHAPTER TWO

"YOU, BOY, YOU—sit correctly; sit in the manner prescribed!" The voice was like rolling thunder; then two heavy hands smote my ears, left—right. For a moment I thought all the Temple gongs had clanged together; I saw more stars than were visible even during the clearest night. A hand grasped the collar of my robe, lifted me to my feet, and shook me like a duster being shaken from a window.

"ANSWER ME, boy, ANSWER ME!" the angry voice shouted. But he gave me no opportunity to answer, just shaking me until my teeth rattled, and my bowl fell out and rolled across the floor. My bag of barley fell, and the thong became untied, loosing a shower of grain into the shocked air. Satisfied at last, the Fierce Man threw me aside like a rag doll.

Sudden silence descended and there was a tense air of expectancy. Cautiously I fingered my robe at the back of my left leg; a thin trickle of blood was oozing from the ruptured scar. Silence? I looked up. An abbot was standing in the doorway facing the Fierce Man. "The boy has been gravely injured," he said. "He has the Inmost One's special permission to sit in the manner most comfortable. He has permission to answer a question without rising." The abbot walked over to me, looked at my blood-reddened fingers, and said: "The bleeding should soon stop. If it does not, visit the Infirmarian." With that, he nodded to the Fierce Man and left the room.

"I," said the Fierce Man, "have come specially from Mother India to tell you the Truth of Buddhism. You in this country have broken away from our tenets and formed your own brand called 'lamaism.' I have come to tell you of the Original Truths." He glared at me as though I were his mortal enemy; then he told a boy to give me my bowl and my now-empty barley bag. For some moments while this was being done, and while my spilled barley was being swept up, he paced around the room as though seeking another victim. He was a tall, lean man, with very brown skin and with a great beak of a nose. He wore the robes of an old Indian Order, and he looked as though he despised us!

The Indian Teacher stalked to the end of the room and mounted the small raised platform. Carefully he adjusted the lectern to his exact requirements. Fumbling in a leather bag which had stiff sides and square edges, he brought forth some remarkable sheets of paper. Thin paper, a hand's span by two hands' span, not at all like the long, thick sheets which we used. They were thin, translucent, and almost as pliable as cloth. His strange leather bag fascinated me. It was highly polished, and at the centre of one narrow side it had a shiny piece of metal which clicked open when a button was touched. A piece of leather formed a highly convenient handle, and I determined that one day I would have just such a leather bag.

The Indian rustled his papers, frowned severely at us, and told us the tale we had long known. I watched in profound interest the way in which the end of his nose wobbled as he spoke, and how his brow formed a sharp ridge as he squinted at the pages. The story he told us? The old familiar one!

"Two-thousand five-hundred years ago the people of India were disillusioned with their religion; the Hindu priests were degenerate, thinking only of earthly pleasures, thinking only of personal gain. The people whom they should have been helping were turning away from their old beliefs, turning to anything that would offer a scrap of hope. Prophets and soothsayers roamed through the land with forecasts of doom and torture. Animal lovers decided that animals were better than humans, so they worshiped animals as gods.

"The more cultured Indians, the deep-thinking men who feared for their country, turned aside from the religion of their ancestors and pondered deeply on the sorry state of Man's soul. One such man was a high Hindu raja, an enormously rich warrior king. He worried and fretted about the future of his only son Gautama, who had so recently been born into a troubled world.

"The father and family had the strongest desire that Gautama should grow up as a warrior prince and later inherit his father's kingdon. An old soothsayer, called in to prophesy, had said that the young man would be a prophet of great renown. To the stricken father, this was 'a fate worse than death.' Around him he had many examples of young upper-class men renouncing a life of comfort and going forth as pilgrims, barefoot and clad in rags, to seek a new spiritual life. The father determined to do everything possible to thwart the prophecy of the soothsayer; he laid his plans.

"Gautama was an artistic, sensitive young man, with a keenly alert intellect which was able to sweep through subterfuge and penetrate to the heart of the matter. Autocratic both by birth and upbringing, he yet had consideration for those under him. His perceptions were such that he became aware that he was carefully guided, shielded, and permitted to meet only those who were personal servants or caste-equals.

"At the time of the soothsayer's prophecy the father had given the strictest orders that his son be at all times shielded from the evils and sorrows which troubled those beyond the palace confines. The boy was not to be permitted to go out alone; his travels were to be supervised, and he should be allowed to meet no one who had poverty or suffering. Luxury and only luxury was to be his lot. All that money could buy was his. All that was unpleasant was ruthlessly excluded.

"But life cannot continue thus. Gautama was a young man of spirit and with more than his share of determination. One day, unknown to his parents, unknown to his tutors, he slipped from the palace and with a carefully chosen servant went driving beyond the palace grounds. For the first time in his life he saw how other castes lived. Four incidents provoked the most profound thoughts and thus changed the course of religious history.

"At the outset of his journey he saw an old, old man, trembling with age and illness, leaning heavily upon two sticks as he painfully dragged himself along. Toothless, blind with cataract, and senile, the old man turned a vacant face toward the young prince. For the first time in his life Gautama realized that old age came to everyone, that with increasing weight of years one was no longer active and supple.

"Badly shaken, the young prince continued his drive, full of strange and morbid thoughts. But there was another shock in store; as the horses slowed for a sharp turn Gautama's horrified gaze chanced to alight upon a miserable figure sitting, rocking, and moaning by the side of the road. A man covered with suppurating sores, emaciated and disease-ridden, was groaning as he picked yellow scabs from his body.

"The young Gautama was shocked to the core. Sick at heart—perhaps physically sick too—he pondered the question as he was driven along. MUST one suffer? Does suffering come to all? Is suffering inevitable? He looked at his servant who was driving. Why was he so calm, the young prince wondered. The driver was unconcerned, as if such sights were common. This, then, must be why his father had shielded him.

"On they drove, with Gautama too stunned to order otherwise. Fate, or Destiny, had not finished, though. At an exclamation from Gautama, the horses were slowed; they came to a halt. At the side of the road was a naked corpse, grotesque and bloated by the fierce heat of the sun. A flick of the driver's whip and a dense cloud of flies, feeding upon the body, rose in a swarming mass. The body, discolored and odorous, was revealed completely to the young man's sight. As he looked, a fly wandered out of the dead mouth, buzzed, and settled again.

"For the first time in his life Gautama saw death,

knew there WAS death at the end of life. The young man mutely ordered the driver to return . . . he sat thinking of the impermanence of life, sat thinking of the beauty of a body which yet had to fall into decay. Was beauty so temporary, he wondered.

"The wheels revolved, the dust rose in clouds behind. The young prince sat in thought, morose, indrawn. By chance, or Fate, he looked up in time to see a well-clad, serene monk striding along the road. The monk, calm and tranquil, radiated an aura of inner peace, of well-being, of love for his fellow men. The brooding Gautama, shocked to the core of his being by the sights he had seen, now received another shock. Were peace, contentment, tranquillity, all the virtues, to be found only if one withdrew from everyday life and became a religious? A monk? A member of some mystic order? Then he, he resolved, would become as that monk. He would withdraw from the life of the palace, withdraw from the only life he knew.

"His father raged and stormed; his mother wept and pleaded. The servant was banished from the kingdom. Gautama sat alone in his room, thinking, thinking. Thinking endlessly of the sights he had seen. Thinking that if he had seen so much in one short excursion—his ONLY excursion—how much more suffering and misery there must be. He refused food, pined, moped, and just sat wondering what to do, how to escape from the palace, how to become a monk.

"His father tried in every way he knew to lift the load of sorrow and depression afflicting the young prince. The best musicians were ordered to play constantly that the young man should have no quiet in which to think. Jugglers, acrobats, entertainers of all types were tried. The kingdom was scoured for the most beautiful maidens, girls versed in the most exotic arts of love, that Gautama should be aroused by passion and thus lifted from his despondency.

"The musicians played until they dropped from exhaustion. The maidens danced and practiced erotic exercises until they, too, collapsed, fainting from exhaustion. Then only did Gautama take notice. He stared with horror at the awkward postures of the fallen musicians. He looked with shock at the naked maidens, pale with the pallor of collapse, with the cosmetics standing out vivid and ugly now that the glow of health had vanished.

"Once again he pondered the impermanence of beauty, how transient it was, how quickly it fled. How sad, how ugly was Life. How garish and tawdry were painted women when their immediate activity had ended. He resolved to leave, resolved to shun all that he had known, and seek tranquillity wherever it might be found.

"His father ranted, doubled, and then trebled the Palace Guard. His mother screamed and became hysterical. His wife, poor woman, collapsed, and all the palace ladies wept in concert. Gautama's baby son, too young to know what was going on, yelled and shrieked in sympathy with the misery around. The Palace Advisers waved their hands helplessly and poured out torrents of words to no avail.

"For days he worked at means whereby he could leave. The palace guards knew him well. The people in the kingdom knew him not at all—for he had so rarely left the palace confines. At last, when he was almost in despair, the thought occurred to him that he had only to disguise himself from his immediate guards. From some friendly servant, who was well rewarded and who immediately left the kingdom, Gautama obtained old and ragged clothes such as the mendicants wore. One night, at dusk, before the palace gates were locked, he donned the old clothes and with his hair tousled and his hands and face well covered with dirt, he shuffled out with beggars who were being turned out for the night.

"Into the forest he went, away from the main roads and people, fearing that his ignorance of the ways of everyday life would betray him. All the night he wandered, striving to reach the limits of his father's kingdom. He had no fear of the tigers and other wild animals prowling at night; his life had been so shielded that he did not KNOW the danger.

"Back in the palace his escape had been discovered. The whole building was searched, the outbuildings, the parks. The king rushed around shouting orders; armed men stood on the alert. Then everyone went to bed to await the dawn when a search could be mounted. In the women's quarters there was wailing and lamentation at the fury of the king.

"Gautama crept through the forest, evading meetings where possible, being silent to all questions when it was not. From growing crops he took his food, living on grain, berries, and fruits, drinking from cold, clear springs. But the tale of the strange wanderer who did not behave as a wanderer should eventually reached the palace. The king's men swept forth in strength, but could not catch the fugitive as he always hid in the thickets where horses could not go

"At last the king decreed that all the dancing girls should be taken to the forest, and they should go in pursuit of Gautama and attempt to lure him back. For days they danced and weaved their way through the forest glades, always in sight of Gautama, always acting out their most seductive dances. At last near the limits of his father's domain, Gautama stood forth and said that he was going into the world in search of spirituality, and would not return. His wife rushed toward him, the baby in her arms. Gautama heeded not her pleas, but turned away and continued his journey."

The Indian Teacher, having got thus far in a story which we knew as well as he, said, "From the then-decadent Hindu religion a new Belief was at that moment formed, a Belief that would bring comfort and hope to many. For this morning we will end our session. This afternoon we will continue. Dismiss!" The others rose to their feet, bowed respectfully to the Teacher and left. I had trouble; I found that my robe had stuck to my leg-scar with dried blood. The Teacher left without giving me a glance. I sat in considerable pain and wondered what to do. Just then an old cleaning-monk hobbled in and looked at me in surprise. "Oh!" he said. "I saw the Teacher leave and I came to clean. What is the trouble?" I told him, showed him how the great scar had burst open, how the blood had poured out, and how I had "plugged the hole" with my robe. The old man muttered, "Tsk! Tsk!" and hurried out as fast as he could with his own deformed legs. Soon he returned with the Infirmarian.

The pain was like raging fire; I felt that my flesh was being torn from the bones. "Ah, my son!" said the Infirmarian. "You are as one born to trouble as surely as the sparks fly upwards!" He sighed, and muttered, "But WHY are some of these Great Teachers, who should know better, so harsh, so unfeeling? There!" he said, as he fastened a herbal compress and helped me to my shaky feet. "There, now you will be all right; I will give you a new robe and destroy the other."

"Ow! Reverend Master!" I exclaimed in some fright, my knees trembling with the shock. "I cannot have a NEW ROBE or everyone will think I am a new boy just joined. I'd rather have this one!" The old Infirmarian laughed and laughed and then said,

"Come on, my boy, come with me and we will together see what we can do about this weighty matter."

Together we walked slowly down the corridor to where the Infirmarian has his office. Inside, on tables, ledges, and shelves, there were containers of herbs, a few powdered minerals, and odd items which I could not then identify. Tibetans only sought medical aid in cases of extreme emergency. Not for us the First Aid kits of the West. We managed as Nature intended! A broken limb would be set, of course, and a very deep wound stitched. We used the long hairs from a horse's tail for stitching, when well boiled they were very suitable. For stitching the very deepest layers we used the long fibres from shredded bamboo. The bamboo was also used as drainage tube when one had to drain pus from an internal wound. Clean, well-washed sphagnum moss made very useful sponge material, and was also used for compresses, with or without herbal ointments.

The Infirmarian took me into a side room which I

had not noticed. From a pile of old and mende
he drew forth one. It was clean, well-mended, a
very sun-faded. My eyes lit up at the sight, for
robe would show that I had been in the Lam
long, long time! The Infirmarian motioned for
take off my robe. I did so, and he examined
other injuries. "Hmmn! Skinny, under-sized. Sh
bigger for your age. How old are you, boy?"
him. "So? Oh, I thought you were three years
Hmmn! Quite a man, eh? Now try on this ro
swelled out my chest and tried to stand straight
look bigger and taller, but my legs would NOT s
The robe was somewhat too big for me and I tr
conceal the fact. "Ah!" said the Infirmarian. "Y
soon grow and fill it up. Keep it on. Good-by!"

But now it was time to eat, eat before the afte
classes. I had already lost much time, so I sh
down to the kitchen where I explained my
"Eat, EAT, boy, and get on with it!" said the fri
soot-streaked cook, helping me generously. The
light streamed through the window. I stood wit
elbows on the frame, looking out as I ate. At tim
temptation was too much, and I flipped a little ts
over the edge of the bowl onto some poor, unsu
ing monk far below. "MORE, boy?" said the
monk in some astonishment."MORE? You must be
low, or"—he winked slyly at me—"are you pastin
heads of the Brothers?" I must have blushed or l
guilty, for he laughed uproariously and said, "
let's mix a little soot with this lot!"

But fun could not last for ever. My bowl was
empty. Below, an increasingly cross group of m
were wiping their black-spattered pates and pe
suspiciously about them. One even started up the
—hastily I withdrew from the kitchen, and saun
as nonchalantly as I could out of the kitchen and
the corridor. As I turned the corner a glowering
appeared and hesitated as he saw me. "Let me
your bowl," he growled. Assuming my most inn
expression, I reached in to my robe and produce
desired article and handed it over for inspection

22

something wrong, sir?" I asked. "That really is my bowl," I continued. The monk examined the bowl carefully, looking for traces of the soot which I had so thoroughly removed. He stared at me with the deepest suspicion, then, as he handed the bowl back, said, "Oh! You are the injured one. You could not have climbed the roof. Someone is dropping wet soot on us, he is ON THE ROOF—I will catch him!" With that, he turned and dashed away toward the roof. I breathed deeply and sauntered on.

Behind me there was a chuckle, and the cook-monk's voice said: "Well done, boy, you should be an actor. I won't give you away or I might be the next victim!" He hurried past me, off in some mysterious mission connected with food supplies, and I continued on my reluctant way back to the classroom. I was the first one there, and I stood braced against the window looking out. It always fascinated me to look out across the country from this eminence. The sight of the beggars at the Pargo Kaling (or Western Gate), and the never-failing thrill of seeing the eternal spume of snow blowing from the highest peaks of the Himalayas, I could spend hours, days, watching.

Around the District of Lhasa the mountains formed a great "U"—the mighty Himalayas which formed the backbone of the continent. Having time on my hands I looked well, making a game of it. Below me the white lime-washed walls of the Potala melted imperceptibly into the living rock of what had once, aeons ago, been a volcano. The lime-white of the man-made structure flowed into the grey and brown of the mountain, and where the one ended and the other began, no man could now say, they had fused together so successfully. The lower slopes of the mountain were covered by the small bushes through which we boys often crawled when trying to escape detection. Lower still were the buildings forming the Village of Shö, with the great courts of justice, the government offices, the government printing works, the civil records offices, and the prison.

It was a busy scene, pilgrims were progressing along

the "Pilgrims' Way" hoping to acquire virtue by stretching their length on the ground, crawling forward a few feet, and then again lying prone. It certainly looked most amusing from my height above. Monks were striding about energetically between the houses—must be the Proctors after a malefactor, I thought—and lamas were proceeding about their stately business on horseback. An abbot and his retinue turned into our road and slowly rode up the wide, stepped path toward the main entrance. A group of fortunetellers plied a brisk trade as they extolled the virtues of their horoscopes—"blessed by a Lord Abbot, mind you, sure to bring you luck!"

The green of the willows in the marsh across the road attracted me; the fronds were gently swaying in the breeze. Pools of water reflected the racing clouds and changed color according to the color of th' passing pedestrians. One fortuneteller was established on the brink of a large pool, and he was pretending to "read the future" of his clients in "the sacred water at the foot of the Potala." Trade was brisk indeed!

The Pargo Kaling was thronged. Small stalls had been erected and itinerant traders were doing a sharp business selling foods and sweetstuffs to the pilgrims. A profusion of amulets and charm boxes were draped over the end of one stall, the turquoise and gold ornaments flashing brightly in the sunlight. Gaily turbaned Indians, heavily bearded, and with flashing eyes, strode around looking for bargains and trying to beat down the seller.

Opposite towered Chakpori—Iron Mountain—slightly higher than the Potala but not so ornate, not so many buildings. Chakpori was austere, somewhat grey and grim. But Chakpori was the Home of Healing, while the Potala was the Home of the God. Beyond the Chakpori the Happy River sparkled and chuckled as it made its swift way down to the Bay of Bengal. By shading my eyes and straining a little, I could see the boatman paddling passengers across the river. His inflated yak-hide boat always fascinated me, and I was beginning to wonder if I would not be better as a boatman than as a small acolyte in a large lamasery. But there was no chance to be a boatman yet, as I well knew, I had to get on with my studies first. And whoever heard of a monk becoming a boatman!

Far off to the left the golden roof of the Jo Kang, or Cathedral of Lhasa, dazzled the eyes as it reflected the sun's rays. I watched the Happy River as it wandered through the marshy land, twinkling through the willow groves, and with a small tributary flowing under the beautiful Turquoise Bridge. Far off I saw a gleaming silver thread diminishing in the distance as the river followed its path towards the flat lowlands.

This was a busy day, by leaning out of the window—with some danger of falling a long, long way—I could see more traders coming along the road from Drepung, coming from the high mountain passes. But it would be some considerable time before they were close enough for me to see details; classes would start before that.

The sides of the mountains were dotted with lamaseries, large ones that were self-contained towns, and small ones which clung precariously to the side of the steep rock pinnacles. Some of the very smallest ones, and the most dangerously positioned, were the hermitages of monks who had renounced the world and were walled into their small cells, there to spend the rest of their life. Was it REALLY good, I wondered, to be so completely cut off? Did it help anyone when a young, healthy man decided to be walled up in a small cell, there to spend perhaps forty years in total darkness, total silence, while he meditated upon life and tried to break free from the bonds of the flesh? It must be strange, I thought, to never see again, never speak again, never walk again, and to have food only every other day.

CHAPTER THREE

I THOUGHT of my Guide, the Lama Mingyar Dondup, who had had to go to distant Pari very suddenly; I thought of all the questions which were welling up in me and which only he could answer. Never mind, tomorrow he would return, and then I should be glad to get back to Chakpori. Here, at the Potala, there was too much ceremony, too much red tape. Yes! I had a lot of questions which were bothering me and I could hardly wait for an answer.

A swelling noise had been for some moments obtruding on my consciousness; now the volume of sound reminded me of a herd of yaks in full charge. Into the classroom erupted all the boys—yes—they WERE playing at being a herd of yaks! I sidled carefully to the back of the room and sat down close to the wall, out of the way of those who raced around.

Round and round they went, leap-frogging one after the other, robes flying, voices raised in shrieks of joy. Suddenly there was a loud "WHUUMPF!" and a gasp of violently expelled air. Dead silence fell upon the room, with boys frozen into position like carved figures in the Temple. My horrified gaze saw the Indian Teacher sitting on the floor, his eyes crossed and unfocused with the shock. Now HIS bowl and barley had been spilled from his robe, I thought with some glee. Slowly he stirred and climbed shakily to his feet, clutching the wall and looking about him. I was the only one sitting, I obviously had had no part in it. Oh! The wonderful, strange feeling to have a perfectly clear conscience. I SWELLED with virtue as I sat there.

On the ground, half stunned, or petrified with fright,

lay the boy who had dived straight at the spare midriff
of the Indian Teacher. The boy's nose was bleeding,
but the Indian touched him with an ungentle foot and
bellowed, "GET UP!" Bending, he grabbed the boy by
the ears and pulled him up. "Disgraceful, horrid little
Tibetan scum," he bawled, slapping the boy's ears in
time to his words. "I will teach you how to behave to
an Indian gentleman. I will teach you yoga that will
mortify the flesh so that the spirit may be freed." I
must ask my Guide, I thought, to tell me WHY some of
these Great Teachers from other lands are so savage.

The scowling Teacher stopped knocking the boy
about and said, "We will have an extended lesson
period to teach you that you should be learning instead
of being ill-mannered. Now we will start."

I called out, "Oh! But Honorable Master, I was
doing nothing at all; it is not fair that I should have to
stay."

The Indian turned a ferocious face in my direction,
and said, "You—you would be the worst of the lot.
Just because you are crippled and useless it does not
mean that you should escape the retribution of your
thoughts. You will stay, as will the others."

He picked up his scattered papers, and I was sorry
to see that the beautiful leather bag, with the handle
across the top and the shiny button which opened it,
had been scuffed by contact with our rough stone floor.
The Indian noticed it and growled, "Someone will pay
very dearly for this; I shall claim another from the
Potala." He opened his case and rifled through his
papers, sorting them out. At last satisfied he said, "We
ended this morning with Gautama stating that he
renounced his life at the palace, stating that he would
continue his life searching for Truth. Now let us continue.

"When Gautama had left the palace of his father,
the king, his mind was in turmoil. He had undergone a
most shatteringly sudden experience of seeing illness
when he had not known of illness, of seeing death
when he had not known of death, and of seeing peace

27

profound, utter tranquillity, and contentment. His thoughts were that as the wearer of the contented look was also wearing a monk's robe, then contentment and inner peace would be found in the garb of a monk, and thus it was that he set forth on his search for inner tranquillity, on his search for the meaning of life.

"He wandered on and on, on into realms beyond those over which his father ruled, on and on following rumors of learned monks and erudite hermits. He studied with the best Teachers that he could find, studying whenever there was anything to be learned. As he learned from one Teacher all that the Teacher could teach him he moved on, ever on, ever in search of knowledge, ever in search of the most elusive thing on Earth—peace of mind, tranquillity.

"Gautama was a very apt pupil. He had been favored of life; he had been given an alert brain and a bright awareness. He was able to pick up information and sort it in his mind, rejecting that which was useless to him and retaining only matter which was of benefit and worth. One of the Great Teachers, impressed by Gautama's readiness and acute intelligence, asked him that he should stay and teach, asked him to become a full partner in imparting knowledge to other students. But this was quite alien to Gautama's belief for—he reasoned—how could he teach that which he did not fully understand? How could he teach others when he was still searching for Truth himself? He knew the Scriptures and the Commentaries of the Scriptures, but, while the Scriptures gave a certain degree of peace, yet there were always questions and problems which broke the tranquillity which he was trying to gain, and thus Gautama wandered on.

"He was as a man obsessed, a man with a burning drive which permitted him no rest, spurring him on and on in search of knowledge, in search of Truth. One hermit led him to believe that only the ascetic life could lead him to tranquillity, so, a rather impetuous man, Gautama tried the life of the ascetic. Long ago he had shed all material things; he had no material pleasures; he lived only to search for the meaning behind life. But now he forced himself to eat less and less, and, as the old, old stories say, at last he managed to live on one grain of rice a day.

"He spent the whole of his time in the deepest of meditation, remaining immobile beneath the shade of a banyan tree. But at last his sparse diet betrayed him; he collapsed through hunger, malnutrition, and lack of elementary care. For long he lingered at the point of death, but no enlightenment reached him; he still had not found the secret of tranquillity; he still had not found the meaning behind life.

"Certain 'friends' had gathered about him during the days of his starvation, thinking that here was a sensation, a monk who could live on one grain of rice a day. Thinking that they would gain great advantages by being associated with such a sensational man. But, like 'friends' the world over, these deserted him in the hour of his need. As Gautama lay near the point of death through starvation his friends one by one left him, wandered off in search of sensation elsewhere. Gautama was now alone again, free from distraction of friends, free from followers, free to start pondering all over again on the meaning behind life.

"This episode was the turning point in the career of Gautama. For years he had been practicing yoga that he might, by mortifying the flesh, free the spirit from the bonds of the body, but now he found yoga useless to him; yoga was merely a means of gaining a little discipline over a recalcitrant body, and had no great merit in assisting one to spirituality. He also found that it was useless to lead such an austere life because continued austerity would merely result in his death with his questions unanswered and his quest unended. He pondered that problem too, and he decided that what he had been doing was like trying to bale out the River Ganges with a sieve, or trying to tie knots in air.

"Once again Gautama pondered; he sat down beneath a tree, weak and trembling, with a weakness which comes upon those who have starved too long and who have but barely escaped from the portals of death. He sat beneath the tree and meditated deeply

29

upon the problem of unhappiness and of suffering. He made a solemn resolve that as he had already spent more than six years in the search for knowledge without gaining the answer, he would sit in meditation and would not rise again until he had found the answer to his problem.

"Gautama sat, and the sun went down, and darkness fell upon the land, and the night birds began their calling, and the animals began their prowling. Gautama sat. The long hours of the night dragged on and soon the first faint streaks of light appeared in the sky, the dawn was approaching. Gautama sat and meditated.

"All the creatures of Nature had witnessed the sufferings of the weary Gautama the day before as he sat alone beneath the great tree. He had their sympathy, their understanding, and all the creatures of Nature considered in their minds how they could help mankind struggle out of the difficult ways into which he had fallen.

"The tigers ceased to roar that their songs and their callings should not disturb the meditating Gautama; the monkeys ceased to chatter, ceased to swing from branch to branch; instead, they sat silent, hoping, hoping. The birds ceased their song, ceased their trilling, and sat, instead, fluttering their wings in the hope of being able to help Gautama by sending him waves of love and waves of cooling air. The dogs, normally barking and chasing around, ceased their noise and went away and hid beneath the bushes, hid where the rays of the sun should not fall upon them. The king of the snails, looking about him, saw the dogs disappearing into the shade, and the king of the snails thought how he and his people could help mankind through Gautama. Calling his people together the king of the snails slowly led the way up Gautama's back, up his neck, and they clustered upon his sun-reddened head, that head so deep in meditation, that head so scorched by the burning rays of the sun; the snails clustered and with their cool bodies protected Gautama from the heat of the noonday sun, and, who knows, those snails

30

by keeping Gautama's head cool may have helped him in his final quest. The people of Nature at one time were the friends of Man; they had no fear of Man, and until Man behaved treacherously towards them, the people of Nature came forward to help Man.

"The day dragged on, dragged on with Gautama sitting motionless, as motionless as a carved statue. Once again the night came, the darkness; once again with the approaching dawn there came faint streaks in the sky, and then the sun brushed upon the horizon. But this time the sun brought Buddha enlightenment. As if struck by lightning, a thought occurred to Gautama, he had an answer, or a partial answer to the problems with which he had been beset. He had become enlightened with a new knowledge; he had become 'The Awakened One,' which in Indian is 'The Buddha.'

"His spirit had been illuminated by that which had occurred during his meditation on the astral plane; he had gained insight and he had remembered the things which he had seen in the astral plane. Now, as he knew, he would be free from the unhappiness of life on Earth, free of returning to Earth in the endless cycle of birth, death, and rebirth. He had gained a knowledge of why Man should suffer, what caused it, what was its nature, and how it could be ended.

"Gautama from that moment became Gautama the Awakened, or, to use the Indian phraseology, Gautama the Buddha. Now he pondered again as to what his course of action should be. He had suffered and studied, and so should he just teach others or should he let them find out by the means by which he himself had found out? He worried, would anyone else believe the experiences he had undergone? But he decided that the only way to gain an answer to this was to talk with others, to tell them the good news of the enlightenment which had come to him.

"Rising to his feet, and taking a little food and water, he set out on the journey to Benares where he hoped that he would find five of those former associates who had left him when he was in dire need of assistance—who had left him when he decided again to take food.

"After a journey which lasted quite a time, for Gautama the Buddha was still weak from his privation, he arrived at Benares and he met the five associates, whom he had been seeking. He talked with them, and gave them that which has come down through history as 'The Sermon on the Turning of the Wheel of the Law.' He told his audience of the cause of suffering, of the nature of suffering; he told them how to overcome suffering; he told them of a new religion which is known to us as Buddhism. 'Buddhism' means a religion of those seeking to be reawakened."

So Gautama knew hunger, I thought. I knew hunger too! I wished that this Teacher would have more understanding, for we boys, we never had too much to eat; we never had too much time to ourselves, and with his voice droning on, droning on long beyond the allotted time, we were hungry, tired, sick of it all, hardly able to take in the importance of what he was saying.

The boy who had leap-frogged into the Indian Teacher sat snuffling; his nose was obviously damaged, perhaps broken, but he had to sit there with his fingers trying to stop the flow of blood, trying to keep from enraging the Teacher further. And I thought then, what is the purpose of it all, why so much suffering, why do those who have it in their power to show mercy, compassion, and understanding—WHY do they, instead, behave in a sadistic manner? I resolved that as soon as my Guide came back I would have to delve more deeply into these problems which were truly perturbing me. But I saw with considerable pleasure that the Indian Teacher was looking a little tired, looking a little hungry and thirsty; he kept shifting from one foot to the other. We boys sat on the floor, all cross-legged except me, and I had to keep myself as unobtrusive as possible. The others sat cross-legged in orderly rows. The Teacher normally patrolled at our backs so that we did not know where he was from moment to moment, but this man, the Indian Teacher, he was shifting from foot to foot, looking out of the window, watching the shadows move across the ground, watching the hours pass by. He came to a decision, he drew himself up and said, "Well! We will have a recess, your attention is wandering, you are not paying heed to my words, words which can influence the whole of your lives and your lives for eternities to come. We will have a recess for one half-hour. You are free to partake of your food, then you will return here quietly, and I will resume my talk."

Quickly he crammed his papers into his leather bag. It snapped shut with a very satisfying "Click!" Then with a flurry of his yellow robe he was gone. We sat rather stunned by the suddenness of it all, and then the others jumped to their feet with alacrity, but I—I had to climb up painfully. My legs were stiff; I had to support myself by leaning against the wall and more or less pushing one leg before the other. But, the last one out, I made my way down to the domain of the friendly cook-monk and explained to him the position, and how I, an innocent one, was being punished as well for the sins of the others.

He laughed at me and said, "Ah! But how about the young man who was dropping pellets of soot? Is it not the case that your kharma is catching up? And is it not the case that if your legs had not been damaged you might even have been the ringleader?"

He laughed at me again, benevolently. He was a nice old man. And then he said, "But go on, help yourself! You don't need me to help you, you've helped yourself long enough. Have a good meal and get back before that awful man loses his temper again." So I had my tea, the same as I had had for breakfast, the same as I had had for lunch—tsampa. The same as I should have for years—tsampa.

We Tibetans do not have watches nor clocks. When I was in Tibet, I never even knew of the existence of a wrist watch, but we were able to tell the time by something within us. People who have to depend upon themselves rather than upon mechanical contraptions develop some different powers. Thus I and my fellows were able to judge the passing of time quite as accurately as those who wear watches. Well before the half-hour had ended we returned to our classroom, returned cautiously, as quietly as the mice which fed so well upon our grain down in the storerooms.

We entered in an orderly procession, all except the boy who had a bleeding nose. He, poor fellow, had gone to the Infirmarian where it was found that he had broken his nose, and so I had the task of presenting to the Indian Teacher a cleft stick in which was wedged a piece of paper bearing the reason wherefore the boy—now a patient—could not be present.

The others sat, and we waited; I standing with my back against the wall bearing the stick in my hand, idly fiddling with the fluttering paper in the end. Suddenly the Indian Teacher appeared in the doorway and glowered at us, and then he turned and scowled at me. "You—boy—you! What are you doing there playing with a stick?" he asked.

"Sir!" I replied with some trepidation. "I bear a message from the Infirmarian." I extended the stick in his direction; for a moment it looked as if he had not the faintest idea what he should do; then suddenly he snatched the stick with such a jerk that I almost fell on my face. Dropping the stick, he took the paper and read it. As he did so his scowl deepened; then he screwed up the piece of paper and flung it away from him, a grave offence to us Tibetans, for we regarded paper as sacred because it was through the medium of paper that we were able to read history, and this man, this Indian Sage, had thrown away sacred paper.

"Well! What are you standing there gaping for?" I looked at him, and "gaped" more for I saw no sense in the way he was going on. If he was a Teacher, then I decided I did not want to be a Teacher. Roughly he motioned for me to get out of sight and sit down. I did so, and he stood again before us and started to talk.

As he told us, Gautama had found a different way of approaching reality, a way which was called "The Middle Way." The experiences of Gautama had certainly been twofold; born as a prince with the utmost

34

in luxury and comfort, with an ample supply of dancing girls (the Indian Teacher's eyes grew wistful!), and all the food he could eat, and all the pleasures he could absorb, then from that, abject poverty, suffering, reaching almost to the point of death by privation, starvation. But, as Gautama readily understood, neither the riches nor the rags had the key to Man's eternal problem. The answer must therefore lie between them.

Buddhism is often regarded as a religion, but it is not a religion in the strict sense of that word. Buddhism is a way of life, a code of living whereby, provided one follows the code precisely, certain results may be obtained. For convenience Buddhism may be called religion, although to those of us who are true Buddhist priests "religion" is the wrong term, the only term is "The Middle Way."

Buddhism was founded upon the Teachings of the Hindu religion. The Hindu philosophers and religious Teachers had taught that the way to knowledge of self, knowledge of the spirit, and the tasks confronting mankind was as one walking along the edge of a razor where the slightest leaning to one side or the other would cause one to topple.

Gautama knew all the Hindu Teachings for he was at the start of his life a Hindu. But by his own perseverance he discovered a Middle Way.

Extreme self-denial is bad, it leads one to a distorted viewpoint; extreme indulgence is equally bad for it equally leads to a distorted viewpoint. One can with profit regard the conditions as those existing in tuning a stringed instrument. If one over-tightens the string of an instrument, such as a guitar, eventually it reaches breaking point so that the slightest touch will cause the string to snap, and there is, therefore, in this over-tightening a lack of harmony.

If one releases all tension on the strings of the instrument, one again finds that there is lack of harmony, one can only get harmony when the strings are correctly and quite rigidly tuned. That is as it is in the case of humanity where indulgence or over-suffering causes lack of harmony.

Gautama formulated the belief in the Middle Way and worked out the precepts whereby one can attain happiness, for one of his sayings was, "Happiness he who seeks may win, if he practice the seeking."

One of the first questions which a person asks is, "Why am I unhappy?" It is the question most often asked. Gautama the Buddha asked why he was unhappy; he pondered, and pondered, and thought of the thing, and thought around the thing. He came to the conclusion that even a newborn baby suffers; a newborn baby cries because of the ordeal of being born, because of the pain and lack of comfort in being born, and leaving the comfortable world which it knew. When babies are uncomfortable they cry, and as they grow older, they may not cry but they still find ways of giving voice to their displeasure, to their lack of satisfaction, and to their actual pain. But a baby does not think about why he cries, he just cries, he just simply reacts like an automaton. Certain stimuli cause a person to cry, other stimuli cause a person to laugh, but suffering—pain—becomes a problem only when people ask why do I suffer, why am I unhappy?

Research has revealed that most people have suffered to some extent by the time they are ten years of age and they have also wondered why they have had to suffer. But in the case of Gautama this question did not arise until he was thirty years of age, for the parents of Gautama had done everything they could to stop him from enduring suffering in any form whatever. People who have been over-protected and over-indulged do not know what it is to face unhappiness, so that when unhappiness eventually is thrust upon them, they are not in a position to deal with the matter and often they have a mental or nervous breakdown.

Every person at some time has to face suffering, and face the reason for suffering. Every person has to endure physical, or mental, or spiritual pain, for without pain there could not upon Earth be any learning, there could not be any purification or driving away of the dross which at present surrounds the spirit of Man.

Gautama did not found a new religion; the whole of the teaching of Gautama, the whole of Gautama's contribution to the total of human knowledge, is focused on or about the problem of pain or of happiness. During his meditation, while the creatures of Nature remained quiet that he might meditate unmolested, and while the snails cooled his sun-heated head, Gautama realized pain, realized the reason for suffering, and came to believe that he knew how suffering could be overcome. He taught these things to his five associates, and the things he taught became the four principles upon which the whole of the Buddhist scripture rests. They are The Four Noble Truths, with which we shall later deal.

The shades of night were falling, darkness was descending so rapidly that we could scarce see one another. The Indian Teacher loomed against the window, his outline limned in the faint starlight. He continued talking, forgetful or uncaring of the fact that we boys had to be up for the midnight service, we had to be up for the four o'clock service, and then we had to be up again at six in the morning.

At last he seemed to realize that he was getting tired, he seemed to realize that standing there in the darkness with his back to the starlight he was perhaps wasting time because he could not see us, he could not know if we were paying attention, or if we were sleeping as we sat.

Suddenly he slapped his hand on the lectern with a resounding "THWANG!" The noise was shattering— unexpected—and we all jumped with fright so that there must have been several inches of air between our bodies and the floor. Then we all fell back with dull, soggy thuds and grunts of surprise.

The Indian Teacher stood there for a few moments, then he just said, "Dismiss," and strode out of the room. It was easy for him, I thought, he was just a visitor, he had special privileges, there was no one to

37

call him to task. He could now go to his cell and rest for the whole night if he wanted to. We—well, we had to go to Temple service.

We climbed stiffly to our feet, and I was the stiffest of all. Then we stumbled out of the dark room into the darker corridor. It was not usual for our classes to be held at such an hour and there were no lights. The corridors were familiar to us, however, and we trudged along until we came to one of the main corridors which, of course, was lit by the inevitable flickering butter lamps, the butter lamps which were set in niches in the walls at head-level, and which it was the constant task of two monks to keep filled with butter and to tend the wick which floated on the surface of the liquid butter.

We stumbled on, up to our dormitory where we fell upon the floor without more ado, trying to gain a little sleep before the trumpets and the conches should call us to the midnight service.

CHAPTER FOUR

I CROUCHED below the great ramparts, making myself into a tightly curled ball while I tried to peer through a slight opening. My legs were raging, searing bars of fire which, I was afraid, would erupt blood at any moment. But I HAD to stay, HAD to endure the discomfort of lying cramped and frightened while I tried to scan the far horizon. Here, in my present position, I was almost on top of the world! I could get no higher without taking wings, or—the thought appealed to me—being lofted by some mighty kite. The wind swirled and howled about me, tearing at the Prayer Flags, moaning under the roofs of the Golden Tombs, and every now and then blowing a rain of fine mountain dust on my unprotected head.

Early in the morning I had stolen out and with fear and trembling made my secret way through little-used corridors and passages. Stopping to listen every few steps, I had with extreme caution at last emerged upon the Sacred Roof, the Roof where only the Inmost One and his very closest friends were free to go. Here there was DANGER. My heart throbbed anew at the thought of it. Here, if I were caught, I would be expelled from the Order in the most dire disgrace. Expelled? What should I do then? Panic welled within me, and for a long moment I was on the point of fleeing down to the lower regions where I belonged. Common sense prevented me; to go down now, with my mission unaccomplished, would be failure indeed.

Expelled in disgrace? What SHOULD I do? I had no home; my father had told me that "Home" was home no longer to me—I must make my own way in life.

My wandering eye caught the sparkle of the Happy River, sought the dark boatman in his yak-hide boat, and my mind cleared. THAT'S what I would do, I would be a boatman! For greater security I edged along the Golden Roof, safe now even from the sight of the Inmost One, should he venture out in this wind. My legs trembled with the strain, and hunger rumbled within me. A patter of rain solved one problem; I bent and moistened my lips on a small pool that had formed.

Would he NEVER come? Anxiously I scanned the distant horizon. I—yes, I rubbed my eyes with the backs of my hands and stared again. There WAS a little cloud of dust! From the direction of Pari! Forgotten for the moment was the pain in my legs, forgotten too was the ever-present danger of being seen. I stood and stared. Far, far away a little group of horsemen was approaching along the Valley of Lhasa. The storm was increasing, and the cloud of dust raised by the horses' hooves was whipped away almost as soon as it was formed. I peered and peered, trying to shield my eyes from the cutting wind and still not miss anything.

The trees were bending away from the gale. Leaves fluttered madly, then broke away and raced windborne off into the unknown. The lake by the Serpent Temple was no longer mirror-placid; seething waves surged along to break madly against the far bank. Birds, wise to the ways of our weather, walked cautiously to shelter, always keeping head to wind. Through the strings of Prayer Flags, now almost breaking-tight with the pressure, came a direful thrumming, while from the great trumpets fastened to the roof below came hoarse bellowings as the wind ebbed and swirled around their mouthpieces. Here, on the very highest part of the Golden Roof, I could feel tremors, strange scrapings, and sudden splats of ancient dust driven from the rafters below.

A horrid premonition, and I turned uneasily in time to glimpse a ghastly black figure rushing upon me. Clammy arms wound around me, choking me, striking me violent blows. I could not scream—I had no breath! A stinking black cloud enveloped me, making me retch with the vile odor. No light, just shrieking darkness, and SMELL! No air, just that nauseous gas!

I shuddered. My sins had found me out. An Evil Spirit had attacked me and was about to carry me off. Oh! I muttered, why DID I disobey the Law and climb to Sacred Ground? Then my bad temper got the upper hand. No! I would NOT be carried off by Devils. I would fight and FIGHT anyone at all. Frantically, in blind panic and furious temper, I lashed out, tearing great chunks out of the "Devil." Relief flooded through me, and I laughed the high-pitched laugh of near hysteria. I had been frightened by an old, old goat-skin tent, rotten with age, which had been blown at me by the wind. Now its shreds were being carried in the direction of Lhasa!

But the storm had the last word; with a triumphant howl a great gust arose which slid me along the slippery roof. My scrabbling hands sought in vain for a hold; I tried to reach the very edge, teetered, teetered, and fell feather-light into the astonished arms of an old lama who gaped openmouthed at me as I appeared— it seemed to him—from the sky itself, borne on the wind!

As was the way of the storms of Lhasa, all the tumult and commotion had died. The wind was lulled and now merely sighed wistfully around the golden eaves and played gently with the great trumpets. Overhead the clouds still raced over the mountains and were whipped to shreds with the speed of their passing. I was not so calm, though, there was MUCH "storm" within me. CAUGHT! I muttered to myself. CAUGHT like the biggest ninny in the Lamasery. Now I'll have to be a boatman or yak herder. Now I'm REALLY in trouble! "Sir!" I said in a quavering voice. "Lama Custodian of the Tombs, I was . . . ."

"Yes, yes, my boy," said the old lama soothingly. "I saw it all, I saw you borne from the ground by the gale. You are blessed of the Gods!"

I looked at him. He looked at me. Then he realized that he was still holding me in his arms—he had been too stunned with surprise to think about it before. Gently he put me down. I stole a glimpse in the direction of Pari. No! I could not see Them now. They must have stopped, I . . . . "Honorable Custodian!" a voice bawled. "Did you see that boy flying over the Mountain? The Gods took him. Peace be to his soul!" I turned around. Framed in a small hatchway was a rather simple old monk named Timon. Timon was one of those who swept the Temples and did odd jobs. He and I were old friends. Now, as he looked at me and recognized me, his eyes widened in astonishment.

"The Blessed Mother Dolma protect you!" he exclaimed. "So it was YOU!!! A few days ago the storm blew you off this roof and now another storm puts you back. 'Tis indeed a miracle."

"But I was——" I started to say, but the old lama broke in, "Yes, yes! We know, we saw it all. I came in the course of my duties to see that all was well, and you FLEW UP OVER THE ROOF BEFORE ME!" I felt a bit gloomy, so they thought a rotting old goat-skin tent, tattered and frayed, was ME! Oh well, let them think it. Then I thought how I had been frightened, how I had thought evil spirits were fighting me. Cautiously I looked about to see if any of the old tent was in sight. No, I had shredded it in my struggles and all the bits had blown away.

"Look! Look!" shrieked Timon. "There's proof! Look at him, LOOK AT HIM!" I looked down at myself and saw I had a string of Prayer Flags twisted around me. Clutched in my hand I still grasped half a flag. The old lama clucked and clucked and clucked, and led the way down, but—I turned abruptly and rushed to the wall peering out again over the ramparts hoping to see my beloved Guide, the Lama Mingyar Dondup, coming into sight in the far distance. But the far distance was blotted out completely by the raging storm which had left us and was now sweeping down the valleys leaving flying dust, flying leaves, and no doubt the remnants of the old goat-skin tent.

The old Custodian of the Tombs came back and peered over the ramparts with me. "Yes, Yes!" he said. "I saw you come up the other side of the wall, you were fluttering in front of me supported on the wind, and then I saw you fall on the very highest part of the Golden Tomb Roof; I could not bear to look. I saw you struggling to maintain your balance, and I covered my eyes with my hand." A good thing, too, I thought, or you would have seen me fighting off the old goat-skin tent, and then you would have known that I had been up there all the time. Then I should have been in trouble.

There was a babble of conversation as we turned and went through the doorway leading to the other buildings below, a babble of conversation. There was a group of monks and lamas, each one testifying that they had seen me scooped up from the lower reaches of the mountain path and lifted straight up flapping my arms. They had thought that I was going to be crushed against the walls or blown straight over the Potala, not one of them had been able to discern through the dust and stinging wind that it was not I being lofted, but part of a goat-skin tent.

"Ai! Ai!" said one. "I saw it myself—with my very own eyes. There he was, on the ground sheltering from the wind and—POOF! Suddenly he was flying over my head with his arms a-flap. I never thought I'd see the like of it."

"Yes! Yes!" said another. "I was looking out of the window, wondering at the commotion, and just as I saw this boy blown towards me I got my eyes full of dust. He nearly kicked my face as he passed."

"That's nothing!" cried a third. "He DID strike me, nearly buffeted my brains out. I was out on the parapet and he came flying by me, I tried to grab him, and he nearly tore my robe off—pulled it right over my head, he did—I was blinded, couldn't see a thing for a time. When I could—he was gone. Ah well, I thought, his time has come, but now I see he is still here."

I was passed from hand to hand much as though I was a prize-winning butter statue. Monks felt me, lamas

43

prodded me, and no one would let me explain that I had NOT been blown onto the roof but almost blown OFF. "A miracle!" said an old man who was on the outskirts. Then—"Oh! Look out, here comes the Lord Abbot!" The crowd respectfully made way for the golden-robed figure who now appeared among us.

"What is this?" he asked. "Why are you so congregated together? Explain to me," he said as he turned to the most senior lama present. At some length, and with much help from the constantly growing crowd, the matter was "explained." I stood there wishing the floor would open and drop me down . . . to the kitchen! I was hungry, having had nothing to eat since the night before.

"Come with me!" commanded the Lord Abbot. The senior lama took an arm and helped me, for I was tired, frightened, aching, and hungry. We went into a large room which I had not previously seen. The Lord Abbot seated himself and sat in silence as he thought of that which he had been told. "Tell me again, omitting nothing," he said to the lama. So, once again I heard of my "marvellous flight from the ground to the Tomb of the Holy One." Just then my empty stomach gave a loud, warning rumble that it needed food. The Lord Abbot, trying not to smile, said, "Take him so that he may eat. I imagine that his ordeal has strained him. Then call the Honorable Herbalist Lama Chin to examine him for injuries. But let him eat first."

Food! It tasted GOOD! "You certainly have an up-and-down life, Lobsang," said the friendly cook-monk. "First you get blown off the roof and thrown down the mountain, and now they tell me you have been blown from the bottom of the mountain to the top of the roof! An up-and-down life, and the Devil looks after his own!" Off he went, chuckling at his own wit. I did not mind; he was always kind to me and helped me in many little ways. Another friend greeted me; a rasping, roaring purr and a hearty butt against my legs made me look down. One of the cats had come to claim his share of my attention. Idly I let my fingers trail up and down his spine, making him purr louder and louder. A slight rustle from the direction of the barley sacks—and he was gone like a flash, silently.

I moved to the window and peered out over Lhasa. No sign of the small party led by my Guide, the Lama Mingyar Dondup. Had he been caught by the storm? I wondered. Wondered too, how much longer he would be returning. ". . . tomorrow, then, eh?" I turned. One of the kitchen hangers-on had been saying something and I had caught only the end. "Yes," said another, "they are staying at the Rose Fence tonight and returning tomorrow."

"Oh!" I said. "Are you talking about my Guide, the Lama Mingyar Dondup?"

"Yes! It seems that we shall have to put up with you for yet another day, Lobsang," said one of the hangers-on. "But that reminds me—the Honorable Infirmarian is waiting for you; you'd better hurry."

I slouched gloomily off thinking that there were too many troubles in the world. Why should my Guide have to stop on his journey and stay perhaps a day and a night at the Rose Fence Lamasery? At that stage of my existence I thought that only my affairs were of importance, and I did not fully realize the great work that the Lama Mingyar Dondup was doing for others. I slouched along the corridor to the Infirmarian's office; he was just coming out, but as he saw me he grabbed my arm and led me back. "Now what have you been doing? There is always some incident or item whenever you come to the Potala."

I moodily stood before him and told him only that which eyewitnesses had seen about the wind and about the great storm. I did not tell him that I was already on the Golden Roof for, as I knew, his first thought would be to report to the Inmost One.

"Well, take off your robe, I have to examine you for injuries and then I have to give a report on your condition." I shrugged off my robe and threw it on a low bench. The Infirmarian knelt and probed and prodded to see if I had any bones broken or muscles torn. He was rather surprised that my only injuries, apart from my damaged legs, were that I was covered with blue-black bruises, some with yellow overtones!

"Here—take this, and rub it well into yourself," he said standing up and reaching to a high shelf, and bringing down a leather jar full of some herbal ointment which had a most powerful stink. "Do not rub it on here," he said. "I do not want to be gassed out; they are your bruises after all."

"Honorable Infirmarian," I said, "is it true that my Guide is having to stop at the Rose Fence Lamasery?"

"Yes, he is having to treat an abbot there, and I do not expect that he will be returning here until late tomorrow. So we have to put up with you a while longer," he said, and then added slyly, "You will be able to enjoy the lectures by our respected Indian visiting Teacher." I looked at him and the thought occurred to me that the old Infirmarian had no greater love for the Indian Teacher than I had. However, there was no time now to deal with that. The sun was directly overhead and it was time I was going to our lecture hall again.

First I went to the dormitory where I stripped off my robe and rubbed in the stinking ointment. Then I wiped my hands on my robe, put it on again, and made my way back to the lecture hall, taking my place at the back as far away from the Indian Teacher as I could.

The other boys came in, small boys, medium-sized boys, and big boys, all crammed in together because this was a special event, a visit by a very noted Indian Teacher and it was thought that we boys would profit by hearing Buddhism as taught by another culture.

As we sat waiting for the Teacher, boys were audibly sniffing. The ones near me moved away, so by the time the Teacher arrived I was sitting in solitary splendor against the wall, with a semicircle of boys not closer than about twelve feet.

The Indian Teacher came in carrying his delightful little leather bag, but sniffing, looking about him suspiciously, his nostrils were working and he was sniffing

46

audibly. Half way between the door and the lectern he stopped and looked about, then he saw that I was sitting alone. He came towards me but soon retreated; the room was quite warm with so many boys in it, and with warmth the ointment was becoming more and more pungent. The Indian Teacher stopped, put his hands on his hips, and he glared at me. "My boy, you are the biggest trouble-maker in this whole country, I believe. You upset our beliefs by flying up and down the mountain side. I saw it all from my own room; I saw you going up in the distance. You must have devils teach you in your odd moments, or something. And now—ough!—YOU STINK!!"

"Honorable Indian Teacher," I replied, "I cannot help the stench, I am merely using ointment prescribed by the Honorable Infirmarian, and," I added, greatly daring, "it is much the worse for me because the stuff is fairly bubbling out of me." Not a flicker of a smile crossed his lips, he just turned contemptuously aside and moved away to the lectern.

"We must get on with our lectures," said the Indian Teacher, "for I shall be very glad to leave you and to journey onward to more cultured India." He arranged his papers, shuffled around a bit, looked suspiciously at all of us to see if we were paying attention, then he continued: "Gautama in his wanderings had thought a lot. For six years he had wandered, spending most of his time searching for Truth, seeking for Truth, seeking the purpose behind life. As he wandered he suffered hardships, suffered privation, hunger, and one of his first questions was 'Why am I unhappy?'

"Gautama pondered the question incessantly, and the answer came to him when the creatures of Nature were assisting him, the snails cooling his head, the birds fanning his brow, and all the others keeping quiet that he should not be disturbed. He decided that there were Four Great Truths, which he called The Four Noble Truths, which were the laws of Man's stay on Earth.

"Birth is suffering, said the Buddha. A baby is born to its mother, causing pain to the mother and pain to the baby, only through pain can one be born to this Earth, and the act of being born causes pain and suffering to others. Decay is suffering; as a man gets older and his body cells are not able to replenish along the familiar pattern, decay sets in, organs no longer function correctly, change takes place, and there is suffering. One cannot grow old without suffering. Illness is suffering; with the failure of an organ to operate correctly there is pain, suffering, as the organ compels the body to readjust to the new condition. Thus, it is that illness causes pain and suffering. Death is the end of illness; death causes suffering, not the act of dying itself, but the conditions which bring about death are in themselves painful. Therefore, again, we are unhappy.

"Suffering is caused by the presence of objects which we hate. We are kept in tension, in frustration, by the presence of those we dislike. We are made unhappy by the separation from objects we love; when we are parted from a dear one, perhaps with no knowledge of when we are going to be with that person again, then we suffer pain, we suffer frustration, thus we are unhappy.

"To desire, and not to obtain that which we desire, that is the cause of suffering, that is the cause of loss of happiness, the cause of misery. Thus, it is that as we desire and do not obtain, then instead we suffer and are unhappy.

"Death only brings peace, death only brings release from suffering. Thus, it is clear that clinging to existence is clinging to suffering, clinging to existence is that which makes us unhappy."

The Indian Teacher looked at us, and said, "The Buddha, our Blessed Gautama, was not pessimistic but realistic. Gautama realized that until one can accept facts, one cannot banish suffering. Until one can understand why there is suffering, one cannot progress along the Middle Way."

The Teachings stressed a lot about suffering, I thought, but I remembered what my own dear Guide, the Lama Mingyar Dondup, had said to me. He said,

"Let us, Lobsang, consider what Gautama really did say. He did not say that everything causes suffering. No matter what the Scriptures say, no matter what the great Teachers say, Gautama at no time stated that everything is suffering. He really said that everything holds the POSSIBILITY of suffering, from which it is clear that every incident of life can result in pain or discomfort or disharmony. CAN! It is nowhere stated that everything MUST cause pain."

There is so much misunderstanding about what great men did or did not say: Gautama had the belief that suffering, pain, went far beyond mere physical suffering, mere physical pain. He emphasized at all times that the suffering of the mind through the dis-function of the emotions was a greater suffering, a greater disharmony, than any mere physical pain or unhappiness could cause. Gautama taught, "If I am unhappy it is because I am not living happily, because I am not living in harmony with nature. If I am not living harmoniously it is because I have not learned to accept the world as it is, with all its disadvantages and POSSIBILITIES of suffering. I can only attain happiness by realizing the causes of unhappiness and avoiding those causes."

I was busy thinking of this, and thinking of what an awful stink that ointment was causing, when the Indian Teacher slapped his lectern again, and said, "This is the First of the Noble Truths. Now let us deal with the Second of the Noble Truths.

"Gautama gave his sermon to his disciples, those who had previously left him when much of the sensation had gone from the Teaching, but now they were Gautama's disciples again. He said to them, 'I teach only two things, suffering and release from suffering. Now this is the Noble Truth as to the origin of suffering. It is the craving thirst that causes the renewal of becomings; the craving thirst is accompanied by sensual delights and seeks satisfaction now here, now there. It takes the form of craving for the gratification of the senses, or the craving for prosperity and worldly possessions.'

"As we were taught, suffering follows something which we have done wrongly, it is the result of a wrong attitude toward the rest of the world. The world itself is not a bad place, but some of the people in it make it appear bad, and it is our own attitude, our own faults, which make the world seem so bad. Everyone has desires, or cravings, or lusts, which make one do things which in a more balanced mood, when free from such cravings and lusts, one would not do.

"The Great Teaching of the Buddha was that he who craves cannot be free, and a person who is not free cannot be happy. Therefore, to overcome craving is to take a big step forward toward happiness.

"Gautama taught that every person has to find happiness for himself. He said that there is a happiness that does not give contentment, it is merely a transient thing and is the type of happiness which a person obtains when he or she wants change always, always wants to flit around seeing fresh sights, meeting fresh people. That is transient happiness. The true happiness is that which gives one deep contentment, gives one's soul release from dissatisfaction. Gautama said, 'When in following after happiness I have perceived that bad qualities develop, and good qualities were diminished, then that kind of happiness is to be avoided. When following after happiness I have perceived that bad qualities were diminished, and good qualities developed; such happiness is to be followed.'

"We, then, have to stop chasing about after the idle things of the flesh, the things which do not endure into the next world; we have to stop trying to satisfy cravings which grow the more we feed them, and, instead, we have to think of what are we really looking for, how shall we find it? We have to think of the nature of our cravings, the cause of our cravings, and having known the cause of our cravings, then we can seek to remove that cause."

Our Teacher was warming up to his subject. He was being a little troubled, too, by the smell of herbal ointment for he said, "We will have a recess for the moment because I do not want to over-strain your mentality, which, I perceive, is not at all the mentality of my Indian students."

He picked up his papers, put them in his case, carefully snapped the lock, and held his breath as he walked by me. For a few moments the other boys sat still waiting for his footsteps to die away in the distance. Then one turned to me and said, "Pooh! Lobsang, you do stink! It must be because you have been mixing with devils, flying up and down to heaven with them."

I replied quite reasonably, "Well, if I have been mixing with devils I should not be flying to heaven with them, but the other way, and as everyone knows I flew up." We dispersed and went our way. I went to the window and looked out pensively, wondering what my Guide was doing at the Rose Fence Lamasery, wondering how I should fill in the time with this Indian Teacher whom I thoroughly disliked. I thought that if he were such a good Buddhist as he imagined himself to be, then he would have more understanding and feeling for small boys.

As I was standing there thinking a young lama came into the room in a hurry. "Lobsang!" he said. "Come quickly, the Inmost One will see you." Then he stopped and said, "Pooh! Whatever have you done?" So I told him about the herbal ointment, and he said, "Let us hurry to the Infirmarian to see what can be done to get rid of that stench before you see the Inmost One. Come—quickly."

CHAPTER FIVE

TOGETHER we rushed down the corridor toward the Infirmarian's office. TOGETHER? No, not quite! The young lama did the rushing, I followed on faltering legs. Followed because he had a grip on the front of my robe and was towing me. I muttered and grumbled to myself as much as lack of breath would permit. I get blown off the ground and onto the roof—and now everyone pushes me around. Ow! I thought, now I am almost BELIEVING that I was blown up. Ow! I wondered what the Inmost One thought—or knew!

We skittered around the corner and swept into the office. The Infirmarian was having tsampa. At sight of us he paused and looked up; his mouth dropped open at seeing me again and his hand hovered between bowl and mouth. "YOU again? YOU? What have you done this time?"

The young lama, gasping with excitement, anxiety, and lack of breath, poured out a stumbling cascade of words—almost tripping over his own tongue with the speed of his speech. "The Inmost One, he wants to see Lobsang NOW. What can we do?" The Infirmarian sighed as he put down his bowl and wiped his fingers on his robe. "He will not merely SEE him, but SMELL him if I take him like this," the young lama muttered agitatedly. "Ai! Ai! What CAN we do to sweeten him?"

The Infirmarian chuckled and then speedily became solemn as he thought of the Inmost One. "Ah!" he said. "I only did it for a joke, I was trying a new ointment and he was available. It is also an ointment which can be spread on posts and walls to keep dogs off by its smell, but it is a 'bruise ointment.' Now, let me think!"

The young lama and I looked at each other in some dismay. DOG repellent, well, it had certainly made ME repellent, but what to do now? So the old man had played a joke on me, had he? Well, I thought, now the joke was on HIM—how was he going to get rid of the smell before the Dalai Lama knew about it? He jumped to his feet and snapped his fingers with satisfaction. "Off with your robe," he commanded. I shrugged out of my robe again. The Infirmarian went into the side room, to emerge minutes later with a leather pail filled with sweet-smelling liquid. Pushing me over a small drain in his office, he up-ended the pail and poured the contents over my head.

I hopped and hopped, the stuff was astringent, and I thought my skin would peel off. Quickly grasping a rag, he swabbed my body, leaving it very pink, very smarting, but sweet-smelling. "There!" he exclaimed with satisfaction. "You have been a great trouble to me, perhaps a painful treatment will discourage you from coming except in dire necessity." He went back into the other room and returned bearing a clean robe. "Put it on," he commanded. "We cannot have you going to the Inmost One looking like a scarecrow." I dressed, itching and tingling all over. The rough material of the robe made matters worse, but the young lama and the Infirmarian did not seem to mind that! "Quick! Quick!" said the former. "We must not waste time." He grabbed my arm and dragged me toward the door. I moved reluctantly, leaving scented wet footprints on the floor.

"Wait!" cried the Infirmarian. "He must have sandals!" With a flurry, he disappeared and then came into view carrying a pair of sandals. I thrust my feet into them and found they were large enough for a person twice my size.

"Ow!" I exclaimed in panic. "They are too big, I shall trip over them or lose them. I want mine!"

"Oh! Aren't you a one?" snapped the Infirmarian. "Just a bundle of trouble, always in trouble. Wait! I must get you fitted right, or you will fall over in the presence of the Inmost One and so disgrace me." He bumbled around, fiddling and fumbling, and then produced a pair of sandals which were of more satisfactory fitting. "Go!" he exclaimed. "Don't come back here unless you are dying!" He turned crossly away and continued his interrupted meal.

The young lama was panting with worry and excitement. "How shall I explain the delay?" he asked, as if I could give him the answer.

We hurried along the corridor and soon were overtaken by another young lama. "Where have you been?" he asked in some exasperation. "The Inmost One is waiting—and he does NOT like to be kept waiting!" This was no time for explanations.

We hurried along the corridors, climbing to the floor above, and the floor above that—and yet another floor. At last we reached a large doorway guarded by two immense Proctors. Recognizing the two young lamas, they moved aside, and we entered the private quarters of the Dalai Lama. Suddenly the first young lama skidded to a halt and pushed me against a wall. "Keep still!" he said. "I must see that you are tidy." He looked me up and down, pulling a fold here, draping a fold there. "Turn around," he commanded, as he eyed me carefully, hoping that I was no more untidy than the average small acolyte. I turned around, with my face to the wall. Again he pulled and tugged and straightened my robe. "You are the boy with the injured legs, well, the Inmost One knows of it. IF he tells you to sit—sit as gracefully as you can. All right, turn around." I turned, noticing that the other young lama had gone. We stood and waited. We waited until I thought my knees would give out. All that rush, and now we wait, I thought. WHY do I have to be a monk?

The inner door opened and an elderly lama came out. The young lama bowed, and withdrew. The high official, for that is who the elderly lama was, looked at me—looked me up and down and asked, "Can you walk without assistance?"

"Holy Master!" I replied. "I can with difficulty walk."

"Then come," he said, turning and slowly leading the way into another room, crossing it, and coming to a corridor. At a door, he knocked and entered, motioning for me to wait outside. "Your Holiness," I heard his respectful voice say. "The boy Lobsang. He does not walk well. The Infirmarian says that he is badly bruised and his legs are not yet healed." I could not hear the reply, but the elderly lama came out and whispered: "Go in, while standing, bow three times and then advance when so instructed. Walk slowly—do not fall. Go in now!"

He gently took my arm and led me through the door, saying, "Your Holiness, the boy Lobsang!" before leaving and closing the door behind me. Blinded by emotion and fright I hesitantly bowed three times in what I hoped was the right direction.

"Come! My boy, come and sit here," said a deep, warm voice, a voice I had heard once before during a previous visit. I looked up and saw first the Saffron Robe glowing softly in a bright shaft of sunlight which streamed through the window. The Saffron Robe! Above it, a kind but firm face, the face of one who was used to making decisions. The face of a GOOD man, our God upon Earth.

He was sitting on a small platform raised above the ground. The red cushions upon which he rested contrasted with the saffron of his robe. He was in the lotus position, with his hands clasped in front of him, and his knees and feet were covered with a gold cloth. In front of him there was a low table containing just a few articles, a small bell, a Charm Box, a Prayer Wheel, and state papers. He had a moustache then, and its ends hung slightly below his chin. His face bore a benign smile, but marks of suffering were there too. Before him, to the side of the small table, two seat-cushions were on the floor. To these he motioned, saying, "I know of your disability, sit in any way comfortable." Gratefully I sat down, for all the rushing around, all the excitement—all these were having their effect upon me and I was trembling slightly with weariness.

"So!" said His Holiness. "You have had some adventures? I have heard much about it; it must have been very frightening?" I looked at him, at this great man so full of goodness and knowledge. Now, I knew, I would HAVE to tell him what happened for I would not deceive him. All right, then I would be expelled—cast out, driven forth for breaking the Law and climbing too high. Never mind, I would be a boatman or a builder of kites or—my mind boggled at the thought—I might even travel to India and become a trader.

The Inmost One was looking hard at me and I jumped in some confusion as I realized he had been speaking to me. "Your Holiness!" I said. "My Guide, the Lama Mingyar Dondup, has told me you are the greatest man in the world and I cannot conceal the truth from you." I paused and swallowed a lump that had come into my throat. "Your Holiness," I said in a faint voice. "I arose early this morning and climbed . . . ."

"Lobsang!" said the Inmost One, his face glowing with pleasure. "Say no more, tell me no more, I already know it, having been a small boy myself oh! so VERY long ago." He paused and looked thoughtfully at me. "This I enjoin upon you," he said. "You are not at any time to discuss this with another, you are to remain silent about the matter of what really DID happen. Otherwise you will be expelled as the Law demands." For a moment he was deep in thought, then he added, musingly, "It is good, sometimes, to have a 'miracle,' for it strengthens the faith of the lower and weaker Brothers. They need what they imagine is proof, but 'proof' examined closely often proves to be but illusion, whereas the 'Illusion' for which 'proof' was sought is truly the Reality."

The mid-morning sun was flooding the room with golden light. The saffron robe of the Inmost One glowed and seemed to be half-flame as a whisper of wind dared to rustle its folds. The red cushions had a halo and cast ruddy reflections on the polished floor. A small Prayer Wheel stirred gently to the vagrant breeze and its turquoise insets ashed little blue beams on the golden air. Almost idly, the Inmost One stretched out his hand and picked up the Prayer Wheel, looked at it speculatively, and put it down again.

"Your Guide, my Brother in Holiness, Mingyar Dondup, speaks very, very highly of you," said His Holiness. "And so do those who know you well. You have a great task in life and you will be more and more in the care of your Guide and of men like him, so you will be withdrawn more and more from class studies and will have private tutoring of a much higher standard." The Inmost One paused and looked at me with a smile lurking at the corners of his eyes. "But you will have to continue that course of Lectures with our Indian visitor," he said.

That shook me; I was hoping to avoid that awful man—hoping to get out of attending the afternoon lecture on the strength of my great experience. The Inmost One continued: "Your Guide will return late tonight or early tomorrow morning, he will report to me, then you will return with him to Iron Mountain to continue specialized studies. The Wise Men have determined your future; it will be hard always, but the more you study NOW the better will be your chances later." He nodded kindly to me, and reached out for his little bell. With a musical sound it rang out, summoning the elder lama, who came hurrying in. I rose to my feet with some difficulty, bowed three times with disgraceful awkwardness—clutching my breast so that my bowl and other items should not fall out as previously—and withdrew backwards almost praying that I should not trip and fall over.

Outside, mopping the perspiration from my brow and steadying myself against the wall, I wondered—WHAT NEXT? The elder lama smiled at me (for I had been blessed by the Inmost One) and said kindly, "Well, now, boy. That was a very long interview for so small a boy. His Holiness seemed pleased with you. Now"—he looked out at the shadows—"now it is time for you to eat and go to your class for the Indian

57

Buddhism Lecture. All right, my boy, you may go. This official will see you past the guards." He smiled at me again and turned aside.

The young lama whom I had first met appeared around a screen and said, "Come on—this way!" I followed, almost tottering, thinking that this day, which was not even half over, seemed a week long already.

So once again I made my way to the kitchen and begged some tsampa. This time I was treated with RESPECT—for I had been in the presence of the Inmost One and already reports had flown that he had been pleased with me! With my meal hastily eaten, and still smelling sweetly, I repaired to the classroom.

Our Teacher stood before his lectern again, saying, "We now have the Third Noble Truth, one of the shortest and simplest of the Truths.

"As Gautama taught, when one ceases to crave for a thing then one ceases to have suffering connected with that thing; suffering ceases with the complete cessation of cravings.

"A person who has cravings usually has cravings for another person's goods, he becomes covetous—he covets that possessed by another, he becomes infatuated with the possessions of another, and when he cannot have those things resentment sets in and the person dislikes the owner of the coveted goods. That gives rise to frustration, anger, and pain.

"If one covets a thing which one cannot have, then there is unhappiness. Actions arising from cravings lead to unhappiness. Happiness is gained when one ceases to crave, when one takes life as it comes, the good with the bad."

The Indian turned over his pages, shuffled about a bit, and then said, "Now we come to the Fourth of the Four Noble Truths, but the Fourth of the Four Noble Truths has been divided into eight parts called the Holy Eightfold Path. There are eight steps which one can take to obtain liberation from the desires of the flesh, to obtain liberation from cravings. We will go through them. The first is:

(1) *The Right Viewpoint:* As Gautama taught, one must have the right viewpoint on unhappiness. A person who feels miserable or unhappy must find out precisely why he is miserable or unhappy; he must investigate himself and find out what is the cause of this unhappiness. When a person has discovered for himself that which is causing unhappiness, then that person can do something about it to obtain the fourth of the Four Noble Truths which is—How can I find happiness?

"Before we can proceed upon life's journey with a tranquil mind and with a hope that we shall lead life as life is meant to be led, we must know what are our objectives. Which brings us to step two of the Holy Eightfold Path:

(2) *Right Aspiration:* Everyone 'aspires' after something, it may be mental, physical, or spiritual gain. It may be to help others, it may be only to help ourselves. But, unfortunately, humans are in very much of a mess, they are undirected, confused, unable to perceive that which they should perceive. We have to strip away all the false values, all the false words, and to see clearly that which we are and that which we should be, as well as that which we desire. We must renounce false values which obviously lead us into unhappiness. Most people think only of 'I,' 'me,' and 'mine.' Most people are too self-centered, they care not at all for the rights of others. It is essential that we look at ourselves as an object to be studied, look at ourselves as we look at some stranger: Do you like the stranger? Would you like him to be your close friend? How would you like to live with him for a lifetime, eating with him, breathing with him, sleeping with him? You have to have the right aspirations before you can make a success of life, and from this right aspiration it follows that you must have:

(3) *Right Speech:* This means that a person must control his speech, must not speak idle slander, must not deal with rumor as if rumor were fact. With right speech one should always give the other person

the benefit of the doubt, and should withhold speech when speech can harm another, giving speech when speech is good, when speech can help. Speech can be more deadly than the sword, speech can be more poisonous than the most venomous poison. Speech can destroy a nation. Thus, one must have right speech, and right speech arises through:

(4) *Right Behavior:* If one behaves in the correct way one does not speak in an incorrect way. Thus, right behavior contributes materially to right speech and right aspirations.

Right Behavior means that a person does not tell lies, does not drink intoxicants, does not steal.

"Gautama taught that we are the result of our own thoughts. What we are now is that which our thoughts have caused us to be in the past. So if we think right now, if we behave right now, we will be 'right' at some near future occasion.

"Gautama stated, 'Hatred does not cease by hatred at any time; hatred can only be conquered by love.' He also said, 'Let a man overcome the anger of another by love, let him overcome the evil of another by his own good.'

"As I was so often taught, one must not give proof of extrasensory abilities, one must not attack those who attack one, for according to the sayings of Gautama, one should not attack those who attack one with abusive language or with sticks or stones. Gautama said, 'If someone curses you, you must suppress all resentment and make firm determination that your mind shall not be disturbed and no angry word shall cross your lips. You will remain kind and friendly and without spite.'

"Our Buddhist belief is of the Middle Way, a code of living, a code of doing to others as one would have done to oneself. The next of the Holy Eightfold Path:

(5) *Right Livelihood:* According to the Teachings of Buddha there were certain occupations which

were harmful to a man, certain occupations which could not be followed by a true Buddhist. For instance, a true Buddhist could not be a butcher or the seller of poisons, nor could he be a slave trader or slave owner. A Buddhist could not partake of nor distribute liquors. The good Buddhist, at Gautama's time, was necessarily a man who wandered alone or lived in a monastery.

(6) *Right Effort:* Right Effort has a special meaning; it means that one must proceed at one's own most suitable speed on the Holy Eightfold Path. A person who is seeking to progress should not be impatient and try to move too quickly before he has learned the lessons which are to be learned. But again, nor must that seeker try to hold back with false modesty, with false humility. A person can only progress at his own allotted speed.

(7) *Right Mindfulness:* It is the mind of Man that controls Man's actions. The thought is father to the deed; if you think of a thing that is the first step to doing the thing, and some thoughts are very disharmonious. Physical desires might distract one and cause one harm. One might desire too much or too rich food; the desire does not give one the pain, but the overeating does. Unhappiness and pain develop from excessive eating, and follow the excessive desire to eat.

The Buddhist must remember that feelings are short-lived, coming and going like the wind which changes at all times. Emotions are unstable things and cannot be relied upon. One must train oneself so that one has the right mindfulness at all times irrespective of one's transient desires.

(8) *Right Contemplation:* As Gautama well knew, yoga was not by any means the answer to spiritual attainment. Yoga is merely a set of exercises which are designed to enable the mind to control the physical body; they are designed to subjugate the body at the mind's command. They are not designed to give one spiritual elevation.

In Right Contemplation one has to control irrelevant thoughts of the mind, one has to know one's own true needs. By having Right Contemplation one could meditate—contemplate—so that without reasoning one could come to a conclusion by intuition as to what was right for oneself and what was wrong for oneself."

The Indian Teacher's voice stopped and he seemed to jerk back into the present. His eyes roved over us and then settled on me. "You!" he said, pointing with outstretched finger. "I want a word with you, come outside into the corridor." Slowly I got to my feet and made for the door. The Indian Teacher followed and closed the door after him, then he opened it again and put his head around the corner saying, "You boys be silent, not a sound from you, I shall be just outside." He shut the door again and stood with his back to it. "Now, boy," he said, "you have been to see the Dalai Lama; what did he say to you?" "Honorable Master," I exclaimed. "I am enjoined not to repeat anything that happened, not to say a word that passed." He turned on me in a fury and shouted, "I am your Teacher, I command you to tell me! Did you mention me?"

"I cannot tell you, sir," I said. "I can only repeat that I am forbidden to make any comment upon what passed."

"I shall report you for insolence and for disobedience, and for being in general a very unsatisfactory pupil." With that, he leaned forward and hit me violently on the left side and the right side of my head. He turned and entered the classroom, his face flaming with temper. I followed and resumed my place.

The Indian Teacher returned to his lectern and he then picked up his papers. He opened his mouth at the same instant as a lama entered. "Honored Sir," said the lama to the Indian Teacher, "I have to ask you to go to the Lord Abbot and I am instructed to continue with this lecture. If you will please indicate the point which you have reached, I shall be glad to continue."

Sullenly the Indian Teacher gave a rough summary of the position, and said that he was about to deal with

Nirvana. Then he said, "It gives me much pleasure that I shall be leaving your class, and I hope my pleasure may be increased by not returning to it." With that he swirled all his papers into his leather bag, snapped it shut with a vicious clank, and swept out of the room leaving the lama looking rather astonished at the display of temper.

We smiled because we knew that things would be better, for this fairly young lama was still young enough to understand the feelings of boys. "You fellows—how long have you been at this lecture? Have you had food?" he asked. "Do any of you want to leave for a few moments?" We all smiled back at him, and assured him that we were not anxious to leave just yet. 'So he nodded in a satisfied way while he went to the window and looked out for a moment or two.

CHAPTER SIX

THE LAMA who was our new Teacher pushed aside the lectern and sat down in the lotus position in front of us, sitting on the slightly raised platform which was present in all Tibetan lecture rooms. At our meals in our dining halls we had high lecterns at which a Reader either sat or stood during meals, because at all times when we ate we were read to so that our minds should be filled with spiritual thoughts while our stomachs became filled with tsampa. It was not considered correct to eat and think of food. It was the custom for formal lectures to be given with the lecturer standing at the lectern, and as we were quick to appreciate, the fact that our new Teacher was sitting in front of us showed us that he was a different sort of a man.

"Well," he said, "you have just been dealing with Right Mindfulness, and I hope that you are in the right frame of mind because the mind is the cause of most of Man's distress. Physical desires can be very troublesome particularly in a monastic community, particularly where the inmates are all celibate. Thus, it is necessary to control the mind—to create right mindfulness, because in creating right mindfulness we are able to avoid the unhappiness which arises when we desire all the things which we know quite well we cannot have.

"You know that the Buddha always taught that men particularly were often led astray by what one might term visual impact. Men, the average man, tends to idealize women." He looked at one rather big boy, and smiled as he said, "I know that a young gentleman such as you, who sometimes accompanies an older monk to the market place, might at times deserve to be called 'Swivel Eyes,' but the Buddha taught that such things are not good for the monk because the desire is father to the action. The thought makes one do things which one knows to be wrong."

He looked at each of us and smiled as he said, "We should take the Middle Way, however, and not be too good and not be too bad. There is a story of a certain wayfarer who was travelling along a road; some time before he had seen a very beautiful young woman pass, and he was most anxious to make her acquaintance. Unfortunately, he had had to step aside into the bushes for a purpose which we need not discuss, and he feared that in the interval the young woman must have passed him by. He saw an old Buddhist monk coming along, and he stopped him saying, 'Will you tell me, Honorable Master, have you seen a very beautiful young woman passing this way in your travels?' The old monk looked blankly at him and replied, 'A beautiful young woman? That I cannot tell you. I have been trained in right mindfulness, therefore it is that I can only tell you that a set of bones passed me some time ago, whether it was that of a man or of a woman I cannot say, for it was of no interest to me.' "

The lama chuckled as he said, "That is right mindfulness carried beyond all reasonable limits, carried in fact to an absurd extent. However, let us carry on with a subject which is very, very much misunderstood."

He went on to tell us that the Eightfold Path had an objective, an objective under which those who followed that Path would attain a very desired end, would attain Nirvana. Nirvana actually means the cessation of craving, the end of resentment and covetousness. The end of covetousness and the other lusts of the body would enable a man or a woman to attain a state of bliss.

Nirvana is liberation from the body, liberation from the lusts and gluttonies of the flesh. It does not by any means imply the cessation of all experience, nor does it mean the cessation of all knowledge nor the cessation

65

of all life. It is incorrect to say that Nirvana means existing in a state of nothingness; that is an error which has been perpetrated through ignorant people talking about things which they do not at all understand.

Nirvana is freedom from lust, freedom from the various hungers of the flesh. Nirvana is not just blissful contemplation, it is, instead, a fulfilment of spiritual knowledge and liberation from all bodily desires. The state of Nirvana is being in a pure state, pure so far as lack of lusts for physical things are concerned. But even when one has attained Nirvana, that is freedom from flesh desires, one still goes on to learn spiritual things and to advance in other planes of existence.

Buddhists believe in the Round of Becoming, they believe that mankind is born to Earth, lives on Earth, and then dies, and then comes back on Earth in a different body, that it is reborn on Earth so that lessons not learned during a past life can be assimilated.

Nirvana is not a place, it is not a place that you can pin down on a map. It is a state of mind, a condition of mind. It is the condition of being thoughtful; thoughtfulness is one of the chief virtues of the good Buddhist, while thoughtlessness is abhorred.

Nirvana does not mean the loss of personal consciousness at the cessation of life on Earth, it means quite the reverse. There is also a further Nirvana which in the Indian language is called Parinirvana.

"A good Buddhist," said our lama Teacher, "is a truly happy person, a person who is concerned with helping others, a person who has thought for others. The good Buddhist does not respect or recognize the titles or castes existing in countries such as India, for a man does not attain a state of happiness by the estate of his parents. A prince could be unhappy, while a beggar could be happy. Birth does not enable one to discover how to defeat the suffering, the state of one's parents' purse had nothing to do with it. The only way to seek liberation from unwholesome desires is by following the practical Eightfold Path which gives one self-knowledge, and as one has self-knowledge one can have lasting happiness."

The lama looked at each of us and said, "I suppose you think that we Buddhists have the greatest number of followers of any religion in the world, you think we are the most important. Well, that is not correct, because at the present time only one-fifth of the population of this world are Buddhists. We have Buddhists in Thailand, Ceylon, Burma, China, Japan, Korea, Tibet, and a certain number in India. There are many different forms of Buddhism, and they all spring from the same source; therefore, it is clear that there should not be friction between us, springing as we do from the same parent. We can each think in our own way. Much later in our lectures we shall deal with the uses of religion, but for the moment I want you to recite the 'Refuges.' "

> *The Three Refuges*
> *I take refuge in the Buddha.*
> *I take refuge in the Doctrine.*
> *I take refuge in the Order.*

The lama said, "You boys must say that in the morning and before retiring at night. You must get it impressed upon your subconscious. You can call it a symbolization of the Great Renunciation which the Founder of Buddhism made when he left the family palace and took up his monk's robe."

"You boys," he continued, "will be renouncing the lures of the flesh. You will be training to be young men of good character, of good conduct, young men of pure thought, for in the days which shall come upon our country, days of sorrow, days of overshadowing evil, for terrible things shall come to pass in our beloved country, it will be necessary for young men of good character to go out into what, to us, is the great unknown and to keep our own culture alive. Therefore, it is that you of this generation must study and purify yourselves, for we of the older generation shall not be able to follow you."

He told us, "In your travels you will meet many Zen Buddhists. You will wonder if their austerities are necessary, for to the Zen Buddhist all those who teach and all that which teaches—such as books or scriptures—are only pointers like a finger outstretched, pointing the Path that one shall take. Think of the people you have seen, think as you look down upon our pilgrims walking around the Ring Road; observe how when some guide or gipsy points to a thing, like one of us at our windows, how a pilgrim's eyes invariably follow and look at the pointing finger rather than the object at which it is pointed. It is a fact that the ignorant always look at the pointing finger rather than in the direction that the finger indicates. This is a fact which was known to the sect of Buddhism which became known as the Zen Buddhists. It is their belief that one can only know truth by one's personal experience of truth. Truth cannot be known by just listening to the spoken word, nor by reading the printed page. One can only profit by actual personal experiences.

"One is enjoined to read, to study the Scriptures, and to listen with attention to the learned lectures of wise men. But all the printed words and all the written words must serve merely as fuel for the workings of one's mind so that when one gets an experience one can relate that experience to great truths as propounded by others." He smiled and said, "All this means that you cannot get far by being a mere theorist, you have to be a practical man as well as a student of the written word. It is stated that one picture is worth more than a thousand words, but I say that one experience is worth more than a thousand pictures."

He hesitated for a moment and turned and looked out of the window. My heart leaped because I thought that perhaps he would see my Guide, the Lama Mingyar Dondup, returning from the Wild Rose Fence Lamasery. But no, he just turned back to us again and said, "I am going to tell you something which undoubtedly will shock you and make you think that Zen Buddhists are uncultured savages, and sacrilegious savages at that! Some time ago in Japan there was a very famous Teacher indeed, a man who was revered for his high ideals, for his profound knowledge, and for the austere manner of his living. Students came from all over the Eastern world to bow at that Master's feet and study under him. One day he was giving a very special lecture in one of the ceremonial temples, a temple adorned by many statues of the Thousand Buddhas, statues cunningly carved from rare exotic woods. The Teacher had the enthralled attention of his students, and then he paused in the middle of his lecture and his students held their breath wondering what he was going to say, because he had, deservedly, a reputation for being very, very eccentric.

"As this wise man turned aside and seized the nearest of the wooden Buddhas and threw it into the fire, the students rose in shocked horror. For a moment there was a babble of conversation, protests, waving hands, and scuffling feet. But the wise man stood calmly with his back to the fire, stood with his back to the blazing statue of the Buddha. When the commotion had ceased he said that everyone has statues in their minds, everyone sets up ornamants, idols, useless things which occupy space in the mind just as useless wooden idols occupy space in a temple. As he said, the only way to progress is to burn up the clutter in one's mind, destroy that which impedes progress. The great Teacher turned and rubbed a finger over one of the higher Buddhas; he turned back to the class and said, 'Here there be dust, dust upon a Buddha, but that is not so bad as dust upon the mind. Let us destroy carved images, let us destroy false ideas that live within us, for unless one clears out one's untidy mind as one clears out an untidy attic, one cannot progress and go on to the higher reaches of The Path.' "

Our lama Teacher laughed outright at our shocked expressions. He said, "Oh! You are a conservative lot! Wait until you get out to some of the other lamaseries, wait until you move among the people. You will find that some have no use for the teachings of religion, and you will find yet others who wash out their mouth before speaking the name of the Buddha, wash their mouths so that their mouths shall be clean before uttering a sacred name. But these are extremes, those

69

who make a fetish of it and those who have no use for religion. Religion is a discipline which is only of use if one uses common sense, moderation, and the Middle Way, and then religion can solve all one's problems."

I do not know, but I suppose I must have grunted or made some sign which attracted his attention, for he hesitated a moment and then slowly came over and stood in front of me and looked down. "Lobsang," he said, "you appear to be very troubled, you have had a most trying, a MOST trying experience today. But from your expression I am sure that there is more troubling you than that, and I am sure also that it is even more serious than that your Guide has not returned, and will not return, this day. Tell me what it is."

I wished the floor would open and drop me all the way through, right down into one of the volcanic chambers because I had to admit to myself I had been thinking rather unusual things. To be quite blunt I was heartily sick of the way I had to live, and I thought that now was the time perhaps. Let us get it over with.

"Honorable Master," I said with some trepidation, "it is true that I am dissatisfied. My mind is in conflict, my thoughts are in turmoil, for I am being driven to take a course of action which is not at all in accordance with my own desires. I have been sorely troubled, and as I sat upon the Golden Roof struggling with the wind, thinking that death awaited me, I was glad because I thought that death would bring the end of my problems."

The lama Teacher looked at me with sympathy. He drew his robe around him and sat on the floor beside me, crossing his legs and setting himself in the lotus posture. "Lobsang!" he said. "Let us discuss this problem, and I suggest that we discuss it with this class because I have no doubt that many of the young men here are similarly troubled at some time or other. I have been at the Potala a long, long time, and perhaps your own problems now may have been my problems in days gone by."

"Honorable Teacher," I replied, "I have no choice,

I had to leave my wealthy home. I was driven out by my parents who were very powerful people indeed, and I was told that I was to be trained in the priesthood. Because I came of a high family I had to undergo more trials and tribulations than had I come from a low family. I had more to learn, I had more to suffer. My left leg was burned to the bone through no fault of mine. Both my legs were broken when I was blown off the mountain in a gale, but although I can barely hobble, although I suffer constant pain, I still have to attend classes. Now, Honorable Teacher, I have never wanted to be a monk, but I have had no choice in what I wanted; I have been forced to do it. Religion offers me nothing."

The lama looked at me with a lot of understanding and said, "But, Lobsang, these are early days. Religion will offer you a lot when you understand the workings of the Middle Way and the rules of this life and the life beyond. Then you will become tranquil and will understand much more what life really is. But at the present stage, what do you want to be?"

"I looked out from the Golden Roof and I saw the boatman on the Happy River, and I thought what a free life that is, how pleasant just paddling backward and forward on a river which everyone loves, meeting interesting people, people who come from India, people who are going to China, people who are going beyond the mountains to return at some time with strange knowledge and strange artifacts. But I—I am just a boy stuck here subject to discipline, not able to do anything that I want to do, always having to obey orders, always having to learn things in which I am not interested, always being told that my life will be hard but that I am working for a special purpose, that I am going to do a special task." I stopped and wiped my brow with my sleeve, then continued, "WHY do I always have to have such hardships?"

The Teacher put a hand on my shoulder and said, "All life is like this classroom; you come here, some of you reluctantly, some of you gladly, but you all come here to learn things, and each of you must learn at

71

your own rate because no one, no teacher, can force your development, for to do so would mean that you had an imperfect knowledge of the subject. You have to progress at your own rate, fast or slow according to your own capabilities, according to your own desire for knowledge. All life is like a classroom; you come to this life as you come to this class. But when you leave this classroom in several minutes' time, it will be the same as dying to this life, dying to the classroom. Perhaps tomorrow you will go to a different classroom, which is much the same as being reborn, reborn in a different body, under different conditions, with different circumstances. You do not know what the teacher is going to teach you, you do not know why the teacher is going to teach you, but when in years to come you go out into the great world beyond our range of mountains you will find that the things you have learned in this classroom and in other classrooms will help you enormously in ways which you cannot at present comprehend."

"This is what my Guide, the Lama Mingyar Dondup, always tells me," I replied. "But I still do not know how I can reconcile myself to doing something which makes me unhappy."

The Teacher looked about to see what the other boys were doing, but the others were all intent, they were interested because it seemed that they all had problems similiar to my own. We had all been put in lamaseries without any choice of our own, in my own case I entered when I was seven. These boys were listening now; we were all, in fact, like people groping in total darkness hoping for a ray of light to guide us.

Our Teacher continued: "You must decide what paths are open to you. You, Lobsang, can stay here and be a monk, or you can leave and be a boatman, or a maker of kites, or a traveller to lands beyond the mountains. But you cannot be all of them at the same time. You must decide what you are going to be. If you are going to be a boatman, then leave this lamasery now and think no more of this lamasery, think no more of being a monk, think only of being a boatman. But if you are going to be a monk—as indeed is your destiny—then forget about being a boatman, devote the whole of your thought to being a monk, devote the whole of your thought to studying how to be a good monk. And the more you think about being a good monk, the easier it will be for you."

One of the other boys broke in, saying excitedly, "But, Honorable Master, I, too, had to enter a lamasery against my own wishes. I wanted to go to Nepal to live, because I think I would be happier in Nepal."

Our lama Teacher looked quite serious, looked as if this was a matter of extreme importance instead of being the idle fancies of boys who didn't know what they were talking about. He replied gravely, "But do you know the Nepalese people very well? Have you had any real experience of them besides the very few you have met? Do you know of the lower types of Nepalese people? If not, if you have not frequently been in their homes, then you cannot know if you would like them. I say that if you want to stay here in Tibet, then you should devote all your thought to Tibet. But if you want to go to Nepal, then you should leave Tibet now and go to Nepal and think no more of Tibet, for if one divides one's thoughts one divides one's forces. We can have a good stream of thought, or force, or we can have the scattered raindrops which cover a wide area but have no force. Each of you must decide what you want to do, what you want to be, and having decided, then each of you must concentrate wholeheartedly and with undivided mind on achieving what you want to be, for if you decide to go to Nepal with one half of your mind and the other half decides to stay in Tibet, then you are in a state of indecision the whole time, you are worried the whole time, and you cannot at any time then obtain peace of mind or tranquillity. That is one of the great forces of the world, one of the great Laws which you must remember. Divide the enemy and you can rule the enemy, stay united yourself and you can defeat a divided enemy. The enemy can well be indecision, fear and uncertainty."

We all looked at each other, and we thought how well this particular Teacher understood us. It was so very much better having a man who was a man, a man to whom we could talk and who would talk back with us and not just at us. We thought of our Indian Teacher, how supercilious he was. I said, "Honorable Master, I have a question: Why is it that some lamas are so very cruel and others are so understanding and so kind?"

The Teacher smiled a little and said, "Why, Lobsang, it's rather late at night to delve into such weighty matters, but I promise you that we will deal with such things, and we will also deal with the uses and abuses of religions. But I think now we have worked long enough for one day, so let's go each of us about his own business." He stood up, and all the boys stood up with him. The lama saw that I was having difficulty so he bent over, put an arm around me, and just helped me to my feet as easily, as calmly, as if he was used to doing it every day of his life.

"Go along, now, boys," he said, "otherwise you will be stumbling and falling in the darkness of the corridors and we don't want any more people who have temporary leg injuries."

The boys all rushed away, full of happiness because we had finished rather more early than usual. The lama Teacher turned to me before leaving and said, "Lobsang, your Guide will be returning in the morning; I doubt if you will see him until the afternoon, or even until the evening, because he has to make a special report to the Inmost One and to the members of the Upper Council. But he has sent a message that he is thinking about you, and the Inmost One has sent a message to him saying how pleased His Holiness is with you. And, Lobsang, your Guide has something for you!" With that he smiled at me, gave me a light pat on the shoulder, turned and left. I stood for a moment or two wondering why the Inmost One should be

74

pleased with me when I was so tattered, and battered, and when in the eyes of others I had caused so much trouble, and I also wondered what my beloved Guide had for me. I could hardly bear to think what he might have for me, because never in my life had I had any gift bestowed upon me. I turned and stumped out of the room just as the old cleaning-monk entered. He greeted me in a friendly fashion and inquired most kindly about my legs. I told him that they were slowly mending, and he said, "I was cleaning in the Lamas' Quarters today and I have heard them saying that the Holy One is very, very pleased with you." I exchanged a few more words, helped the old man light the butter lamps, and then I went on my way, going down and down, reluctantly passing the corridor to the kitchens and going, instead, into one of the minor temples. I wanted to be alone, wanted to think, wanted to meditate on the past and contemplate the future.

In a lamasery there is little privacy for an acolyte—or more accurately, a chela—because chela is the Buddhist term—and if we ever were overcome with sorrow or problems, then the only place that we could be alone was in one of the minor temples where we could get behind one of the larger of the Sacred Figures where no one would disturb us. So I went down and entered a dimly lit temple where the butter lamps were sputtering, showing that someone had got water in with the butter, the lamps were sputtering and sending up clouds of black smoke which were leaving marks on the walls, leaving marks on a tanka.

I walked on and on, past the smoldering incense burners, and turned to my favorite statue and sat down beneath its shadow. As I sat there was a "Urrah, Urrah" and a friendly black head butted me in the small of my back, and then great furry feet made their way onto my lap and started knitting, while the cat went on purring louder and louder.

For some moments I played with the old cat, rubbing his fur, pulling his tail and tweaking his ears, and all the time he purred louder and louder. Then suddenly, like a lamp going out, his head dropped and he fell asleep on the lap of my robe. I clasped my hands and thought of all the incidents of my life, thought of all the difficulties. I pondered about the present, thinking how easy it was for people to give one platitudes about religion, thinking how easy it was for one to say of the Rules of Right Living. But it was not so easy when one was a small boy and had just been forced into a career or vocation without the slightest inclination or desire for such career or vocation. So thinking, I must have drifted off to sleep, sitting upright as we often did when we slept. The old cat slept, and I slept as well, and time passed us by. The lengthening shadows outside became darker and darker; the sun ran its course and disappeared. Soon over the edge of the mountains peered the face of the silver moon, and all the houses of Lhasa had the little butter lamps flickering behind their windows. And I and the old cat, we slept in the shadow of the Sacred Figure.

CHAPTER SEVEN

A DEEP droning buzz penetrated my sleeping mind. Somewhere nearby, very much thought-power was being poured into the receptive air. My telepathic powers were stirred. I lifted my nodding head and tiredly opened my drooping eyelids. My! I was tired! A slight stir on my lap, and a loving mouth took a gentle grip of my hand and squeezed with affection. "Aurragh! Mmmrrno!" said the old guardian cat. He looked up at me with deep understanding. The faint flicker of a butter lamp reflected blood red from eyes that were sky blue by daylight. Softly, so softly that I was aware of it only after he had left, the cat slid from my lap and merged with the palpable shadows.

Oh! My legs were stiff: the scarce-healed bones felt as if they were grating, the tight, deep burn-scar gave the impression that it would at any moment peel away from the flesh to leave again a raw and gaping wound. Waves of pain shot up my limbs and twirled fierce talons of pain along my spine, threatening to tear my ribs from their seatings. I lay still, gasping. As the spasm slowly faded I cautiously looked about me. Here, in the deep purple shadow of the great Sacred Figure I could see, unseen.

The windows were outlined as dark rectangles on a wall of dancing shadows. Through the glassless frames I could see the night sky as a black pall of smoothest velvet sprinkled with bright jewels of light. Diamonds, rubies, and turquoise dots twinkled and swirled above. Here, in the high thin air of Tibet, stars were seen in color, not like white specks of light as in lower parts of the world. Here there were no rolling clouds of smoke to sully the purity of the sky and obscure the grandeur of the heavens. Mars was red—a pale ruby, Venus was green, while the little speck of Mercury was as a splinter of turquoise. Faint finger marks as of finely crushed diamond dust stretched in a band as far as I could see. Tonight there was no moon to compete with and swamp the feeble starlight.

On the walls the shadows leaped and postured, now being of giant figures stretching to the roof, now squat dwarfs scrabbling on the floor. Off to the side near me a butter lamp was damaged. From its battered bottom there came a "gluck-gluck" as melted butter seeped out, then a "splatt!" as the congealing liquid spattered on the floor. Against a distant wall by the side of a window a tanka fluttered almost as though it were a moth straining to reach the flickering flames. It clattered slightly as it bulged away from the wall, vibrated, and then sank back as exhausted, only to repeat again and again. For a moment I had what was almost an attack of vertigo; I had awakened suddenly from sleep, and now as I looked about, the shadows moving and writhing and twisting, and the different cadences of the voices on the other side of the Sacred Figure rather bemused me. I looked up, up at the back of the head of the great figure behind which I crouched. For a moment I felt panic, the figure was toppling, toppling, it was going to fall on me and crush me. The outlines wavered, and I got ready to throw myself sideways, hampered as I was by my damaged legs. But suddenly—I almost laughed out loud—it was the illusion of life through the flickering of the shadows.

By now the pain had somewhat subsided. I got on my hands and knees and softly crept around the edge of the figure, so that I could peer into this, one of the innermost of the temples. I had never seen a service in this temple before; we boys were rigidly excluded, for us it was the main temple, or one of the more common of the minor temples, but this, hollowed in the rock far beneath the man-made structure, I wondered what it was, what they were doing here. Cautiously, pulling my robe around my waist so that I should not trip over it, I edged forward and peered round the corner.

This was interesting, I thought. In front of me in a circle were nine lamas all in their saffron robes, all with their heads facing the center of the circle, and in the center upon an ornately carved stand was Something—Something which I could not clearly distinguish. There seemed to be something, and yet there seemed to be nothing there. I shivered, and the shaven hair of my head stood rigidly erect like guards on parade, for the chill fingers of fear had reached out and touched me, stimulating me so that I was ready to flee. I thought that on that carved stand stood a creature from the shadow world, a creature which had no real existence in this, our world, and hardly any existence in the other world from whence it came. I stared and stared.

It seemed to be a globe of something, or a globe of nothing; it seemed to be almost without form, and yet what form there was rippled! I wished I could go closer, and peer over the head of one of the seated lamas, but that would be sure detection. So I sat back, rubbed my hands into my eyes trying to wipe away sleep, trying to make them more alert, trying to make them see better in this haze and gloom. Satisfied that I had done as much as I could to my eyes, I crouched forward again on hands and knees, and stared, shifting my position slightly to get a better view between the shoulders of two lamas.

I saw—it occurred to me suddenly—that this was an enormous rock crystal, flawless, perfect. It reposed upon its carved stand and commanded the attention of the lamas who sat almost in devotion before it. They eyed it intently, and yet not so intently as to engage their physical eyes, but instead it seemed to be a use of the third eye. Well, I thought, I, too, am clairvoyant. So I stared no more with my eyes; instead, I let my clairvoyant faculties come into play, and in the crystal I saw colors, swirls, whorls, and a smoky turbulence. Amazingly, frighteningly, I seemed to be falling, falling from an immense height, falling from the top of the world down into an abyss. But, no, it was not an abyss; instead, a world was stretching out in front of me, a world where there were different colors, different standards. I saw, as from a slight eminence, people wandering about full of misery, full of sadness; some were full of pain. They were lost souls, souls without guidance, souls pondering a method of release from their worries.

As I sat there entranced, as though I were on the sunlit plane of a different world, the chants of the lamas droned on. Every so often one would reach out a hand and ring a silver bell, another opposite would do the same with a different tone of bell. And so they would go on with their chants, their music sliding up and down the scale, not in notes staccato as in other parts of the world, but here a glissade of notes, sliding one into the other, merging into chords which echoed from the walls and reverberated and made chords of their own.

The leader of the lama group clapped his hands; the one next to him rang a bell, and the third of the group lifted up his voice in a ritualistic chant, "Oh! Listen to the Voices of our Souls." And so they went on from one to the other repeating the age-old stanzas, first one at a time, then in unison, the cadence of their voices rising and falling, rising and falling, lifting me out of time, out of myself.

Then came the whole set of prayers of this group:

Oh! Listen to the Voices of our Souls,
All you who cower in the wilderness, unprotected.
Listen to the Voices of our Souls
That we may protect the unprotected.
As the First Stick of Incense is lit and the smoke
rises upward
Let your Soul and your Faith rise also,
That you may be protected.

. . . . . .

Oh! Listen to the Voices of our Souls,
All you who cringe with fear in the night.
Listen to the Voices of our Souls,

For we will be as a lantern glowing in the dark-
     ness
That we may guide benighted wayfarers.
     As the Second Stick of Incense is lit and glows with
          life
Let your Soul perceive the Light we shine that you
          may be guided.
Oh! Listen to the Voices of our Souls,
     All you who are stranded at the Gulf of Ignorance.
Listen to the Voices of our Souls,
     Our help shall be as a bridge to cross the chasm,
To assist you farther on the Path.
     As the Third Stick of Incense is lit and the smoke
          trails,
Let your Soul step forth bravely into Light.

          •   •   •   •   •

Oh! Listen to the Voices of our Souls,
     All you who are faint with the weariness of Life.
Listen to the Voices of our Souls,
     For we bring you Rest that rested your Soul shall
          sally forth anew.
As the Fourth Stick of Incense is lit and the smoke
          idly drifts,
We bring Rest that, refreshed, you may rise renewed.

          •   •   •   •   •

Oh! Listen to the Voices of our Souls,
     All you who scoff at Holy Words.
Listen to the Voices of our Souls.
     We bring you Peace! That you may dwell upon Im-
          mortal Truths.
As the Fifth Stick of Incense is lit to bring fragrance
          to Life,
     Open your mind that you may KNOW!

The sound of the chanting died away. A lama raised
his bell and tinkled it softly; others picked up their
bells and tinkled them. First they all rang separately,
and then, according to some prearranged pattern, they
all rang out together, forming a special tonal scheme
which echoed and reverberated, and varied in pitch
and intensity. The lamas continued their deep droning,
repeating again, "Oh! Listen to the Voices of our

Souls," ringing their bells, droning on. The effect was hypnotic, mystical.

I continued to look at the people about me—or were they about me? Was I in some other world? Or was I looking into a crystal? My strong impression was that I was in another world where the grass was greener, where the sky was bluer, where everything stood out in sharp, vivid contrast. There was the green sward beneath my feet—good gracious, I could feel it with my bare toes! I could feel moisture seeping through my robe where my knees were in contact. My hands, too, as I gently scuffed them seemed to feel grass and perhaps here and there a stone or two. I looked about me with avid interest. There were great boulders in the foreground, of a greenish stone, here and there streaked with white veins. Other boulders were of different colors; one to which I was particularly attracted was of a reddish hue, reddish with milk-white strands running through it. But what impressed me most was the manner in which everything stood out with stark reality, the manner in which everything looked more normal than normal, with brighter colors, with sharper outlines.

There was a gentle breeze blowing; I could feel it above my left cheek. It was rather astonishing because it bore upon it strange scents, exotic odors. Some distance away I saw something that looked like a bee. It was buzzing along, and it landed and entered the trumpet of a little flower growing in the grass. All this I saw without consciously being aware of the passage of time, but then I became alarmed, wary, for there was a whole group of people coming my way. I looked at them and I was powerless to move; they were coming toward me and I was more or less in their path. Here, as I looked at them, I sensed something very much amiss. Some of the people were old people who leaned upon sticks and who hobbled along barefoot, clad in tattered rags. Others were obviously men of wealth, but not with the general air of well-being which affluence usually brings, for one thing stood out particularly about these men and women—they were miserable, frightened, the slightest movement made them jump and clasp their hands across their breasts. They looked nervously about them, and not one seemed to be aware of his neighbor; they seemed to feel that they were alone, forgotten, desolate, and abandoned in some alien world.

They came on, each one an individual aware only of his own existence, and yet they came in a group, no one touching another, no one aware of the presence of another. They came on lured by the voices which I, too, could hear: "Oh! Listen to the Voices of our Souls, all you who wander unguided." The chant and the droning went on and the people came on also, and as they came to a certain spot—I could not see what actually was happening—each face lit up with a sort of unearthly joy, each person stood more erect as if he or she had received an assurance and felt the better therefore. They moved along out of my sight. Suddenly there was a clash of bells in dissonance, and I felt a violent jerk within me as if someone was reeling me in, as if I was a kite at the end of a string being drawn in against a gale which tried to loft it further.

As I looked out upon that strange landscape I had the impression that night was falling, for the sky was darkening and the colors were becoming less distinguishable. Things seemed to be shrinking. Shrinking? How could they shrink? But undoubtedly they were shrinking, and not only were they becoming smaller but a fog like the clouds above was beginning to cover the face of that world, and as my horrified gaze took in the scene getting smaller and smaller, the fog changed into black thunder clouds shot with lightning.

The world was getting smaller and smaller, and I was rising upward and upward. As I looked down I could see it rotating beneath my feet, and then I decided of course it was not rotating beneath my feet because I was on my hands and knees in the temple. Or where was I? I was confused and dazed, and then once again came that sharp, terrific jerk, a jerk which nearly spun my brain out of my head.

Quite dizzy for the moment, I raised my hand to rub

my eyes. And then I gazed again, and I saw before me that the crystal was a crystal once again, no longer a world, just a crystal lying dull and lifeless with no point of light within it. It stood upon its carved base as though it were a stone, or an idol, or anything; not as the most wonderful instrument of wonderful experiences. Slowly a lama rose to his feet and took from the base a cloth—it looked like black velvet. Reverently he unfolded the cloth and draped it over the crystal and then tucked it in. He bowed three times in the direction of the crystal, and turned away to resume his seat. As he did so his astonished gaze fell on me. For some seconds there was a stunned, shocked silence; time itself seemed to have been paralyzed. I could just hear my heart give one loud "thump!" and then no more. There was an impression that the whole of nature, the whole of time, was listening in hushed suspense to see what would happen next.

There was a mutter between the lamas. The one nearest me stood up and towered over me. He was the biggest of the lot, but to my terrified eyes he looked bigger than the Potala itself. He towered over me and started to speak, but then another lama recognized me. "It is Mingyar's boy, Lobsang," he said, rather relieved. "This is our most telepathic boy. Bring him here." The giant lama reached down and put his hands beneath my arms and lifted me up, for being told that I was "Mingyar's boy" had given him the knowledge that I could not easily walk, and so he saved me that trouble. He carried me into the circle of lamas, each one looking at me as if they were going to peer into my soul, as if they were going to peer through my soul, beyond, and into other realms leading to the Overself.

I was in a considerable state of fright because I did not know that I had done anything particularly wrong. I had chosen this particular temple because some of the others were always thronged by small boys who were not seriously interested in meditation. I was. But what was that? "Lobsang!" said a small, wizened lama. "What were you doing here?"

"Honorable Master," was my reply. "It has long

been my habit to come to the minor temples for private meditation, and I sit behind one of the Sacred Figures where I cannot disturb anyone else who is meditating. I had no thought of intruding upon your service; in fact"—I looked rather shamefaced—"I fell asleep, and I was only awakened when I heard your service about to start."

Off to the left the leaking butter lamp had ceased its "splat! splat!" and suddenly there came a short hiss as the floating wick, now deprived of liquid butter, expired and was extinguished against the metal. For seconds it smoldered red, and then there was the acrid, rancid smell of charring wick. From outside our circle came a familiar "Mrrow! Mmrrow!" friend cat importantly pushed his way between two lamas, walked to me with tail erect and butted me in friendship. I reached out a trembling hand and rifled my fingers through his fur. He turned to me, gave another butt, and said "Aarrah!" and sedately stalked off, pushing his way between two more lamas. The lamas looked at each other, and a faint smile played about their lips. "So, our guardian here knows you well, Lobsang! He spoke, well for you, too; he assured you of his devotion and told us that you had spoken the truth."

For a few moments there was silence. One of the younger lamas turned his head and saw the cat haughtily stalking away. He chuckled and turned back to the group. The old, wizened lama, who seemed to be very much the senior, and who was in charge of the service, looked at me, then turned to each of his fellows, remarking, "Yes, I remember; this is the boy who has to have special instruction. We were waiting for the return of his Guide before summoning him here, but as he is here let us test his experience and his capabilities so that we may assess him without the influence of his powerful Guide." There was a murmured agreement, and low-voiced suggestions which I was far too confused to follow. These were the high telepathic lamas, the high clairvoyants, the ones who helped others, and now I was sitting with them—sitting shivering with fright it is true, but still sitting with them. One of them turned to me and said, "Lobsang, we have heard so much about you, about your innate powers, about your possibilities, and about your future. In fact, it is we who investigated the Record of Probabilities to see what would happen in your case. Now, are you willing to undergo some ordeal in order that we may determine the extent of your powers? We want to take you for a walk in the astral, and in the world below the astral, we want to take you as a ghost through our Potala."

I looked at him dubiously. Take? How did they think I could walk? I could hobble about the corridors, but my legs were not yet healed enough to enable me to WALK with any degree of confidence.

I hesitated, thought about it, and twisted the hem of my robe. Then I replied, "Honorable Masters! I am very much in your power, but I have to say that I am not able to walk much because of my accidents; but, as a good monk should, I place myself at your disposal, hoping that my Guide, the Lama Mingyar Dondup, would approve of my decision." No one laughed, or even smiled, at what must have sounded like a very pompous statement, for I was young and inexperienced, and after all I was doing my best and who can do more than one's best.

"Lobsang, we want you to lie prone, we have to have you prone because your legs will not permit you to be in the orthodox position. Therefore, you must lie prone." The old lama carefully took a seat-cushion and placed it beneath my head, then he placed my hands with fingers clasped so that my two hands with fingers entwined were between the end of the breast bone and the umbilicus. Then they rearranged themselves; they shifted the crystal to one side, reverently placing it in a place that I had not previously noticed, in the base of a Sacred Figure. They sat around me so that my head was in the exact center of the circle. One lama broke away from the group, and returned with sticks of incense and a small brazier. I almost disgraced myself by sneezing as a trailing cloud of smoke crossed my face and made my nostrils itch.

Strangely, my eyes were getting heavy. I had a sense of increasing lassitude, but the lamas were not looking at me, they were looking at a point far above me. I forced open my eyes, and I could see under their chins, I could see up into their nostrils, their heads were so far tilted that I could not distinguish their eyes. No, they were not looking at me, they were looking—Where?

The incense smoldered on, making a small sizzling noise which I had not noticed before. Suddenly I clutched my hands even more tightly because the whole building seemed to be rocking. I had heard of earthquakes, and I thought that suddenly we of the Potala were being afflicted with an earthquake. Panic welled up within me and by great effort I managed to suppress it, thinking that it would be a disgrace to my Guide if I scrambled to my feet and scuttled out of the temple while the lamas sat placidly on.

The swaying continued, and for a moment I felt almost sick. For a moment I felt that I was drifting up, I found that one of the beams of the roof was a few inches from my hand. Idly I put out my hand to ward myself off, and to my terror my hand went right through the beam, not even disturbing the dust which lay upon its surface.

With the terror of that experience, I sank down rapidly and landed on my feet by the side of a Sacred Figure. Quickly I put out my hand to steady myself, knowing that my legs would not support me. But again, my hands went right through the Sacred Figure, and my legs felt firm and strong; I had no pain, no discomfort. I turned quickly—the group of lamas was still there. But, no! One was absent. He was, I perceived, standing beside me and his hand was about to touch my elbow. He appeared bright, he appeared rather larger than the others, and when I looked at the Sacred Figure I found that I, too, was a bit larger than my normal state. Again, a great knot of fear seemed to be inside me and my stomach churned with fright. But the lama took my elbow, reassuring me with, "It is all right, Lobsang, there is nothing for you to fear. Come with me." He led the way with his hand on my right elbow. Carefully we skirted the lamas still sitting in a circle. I looked, and I looked in the center of the circle, but my body was not there; there was nothing there. Carefully I felt myself, and I felt solid. Surreptitiously I reached out and touched the lama beside me, and he was solid too. He saw my gesture and laughed and laughed. "Lobsang! Lobsang! You are now in a different state complete with your body. Only those with the greatest occult ability, inborn ability, can do such a thing as that. But come with me."

We walked to the side of the temple, and the wall came closer and closer. I withdrew from his grasp and tried to turn aside, exclaiming, "No. We shall hurt ourselves unless we stop. This wall is solid!"

The lama regained his grip on me and commanded, "Come along! When you have more experience you will discover how simple this is!" He moved behind me and put his hands between my shoulder blades. The wall loomed ahead, a solid wall of grey stone. He pushed, and truly the most remarkable sensation of my life came upon me as I entered the stone of the wall. It seemed as if my whole body was tingling, it seemed as if millions—billions—of bubbles were bouncing against me, not impeding me, just tickling me, just making my hair stand on end, just making me itch pleasantly. I seemed to be moving without any difficulty whatever, and as I looked I had the impression that I was moving through a dust storm, but the dust was not hurting me, it was not troubling my eyes at all, and I put out my hands and I tried to grasp some of the dust. But it went through me—or I went through it, I do not know which is correct. The lama behind me chuckled and pushed a little harder, and I broke right through the wall and into the corridor beyond. An old man was coming down carrying a butter lamp in each hand, and carrying something pressed between his left elbow and his body. I tried to avoid contact with him, but it was too late. Immediately I was set to apologize for my clumsiness, but the old man went on; he had walked through me, or I had walked through him, and neither of us was aware of the contact, neither had the slightest impression that he had just walked through another human.

With the lama guiding me, we moved through the building, never intruding upon the privacy of others alone in their rooms, but instead visiting storerooms and—a rather caustic comment or gesture on the part of the lama who knew me so well—we visited the kitchen!

The old cook-monk was there, resting against a great leather container of barley. He was scratching himself and picking his teeth with a piece of stalk from somewhere; every so often he would turn and spit into the corner, and then get back to his scratching and his teeth-picking. Eventually, as we stood watching him, he turned around, gave a hearty sigh, and said, "Ai! Ai! Time again to prepare food, I suppose. Oh! What a life this is; tsampa, tsampa, and yet more tsampa, and all these hungry people to fill!"

We moved on and on through the building. My legs did not trouble me at all; in fact, to be truthful about it, I did not even think about my legs, for there was no reason that I should—they did not disturb me. We were careful, very careful, not to invade the privacy of another person. We turned the corridors as much as we could so as not to enter any individual living space. We came, deep down, into the storerooms. Outside there was my old friend, Honorable Puss Puss, lying stretched out full length on his side, twitching slightly. His whiskers were quivering and his ears were flat upon his head. We were approaching soundlessly, we thought, but suddenly he awoke to full alertness and sprang to his feet bristling and with bared fangs. But then his eyes went crossed as he looked at the astral plane (as all cats can), and he started to purr as he recognized me. I tried to pat him, but of course my hand went right through him, a most remarkable experience, for I often patted old Honorable Puss Puss and never before had my hands gone inside. He seemed as amused as I was distressed, but he just gave a butt at me, which went through me to his surprise this time, and then he dismissed the whole thing from his mind, lay down, and went to sleep again.

For a long time we wandered through solid walls, rising up through floors, and then at last the lama said, "Down again, let us go down, for we have journeyed far enough on this occasion." He took my arm, and we sank down through a floor, appearing from the ceiling beneath, and through another floor, until we came to the corridor off which the temple lay. Once again we approached the wall, but this time I had no hesitation, I walked through it, rather reveling in the strange sensation of all those bubbles coming, all that pleasant tickling. Inside, the lamas were still in their circle, and my lama—the one who was holding my arm—told me that I should lie down in the position I originally occupied. I did so, and on the instant sleep came upon me.

CHAPTER EIGHT

SOMEWHERE a bell was tolling. Muted at first by distance, it rapidly grew in volume. "CLANG! CLANG!" it went. Strange, I thought, a BELL? Good gracious, it is tolling in time with my heartbeat. For a moment panic threatened to overwhelm me; had I overslept and been late for Temple service? Blearily I opened my eyes and tried to see where I was. This was STRANGE! I could not focus. All I could discern was nine horrible white blobs stuck on the top of saffron streaks. My brain creaked with the effort of thought. Where was I? What happened? Had I fallen off a roof or something? Drearily I became aware that there were various aches and pains surging back into my consciousness.

Ah, yes! It all came back with a rush, and with the knowledge came the ability to focus my eyes and see what was before me. I was lying on my back on the cold, cold stone floor. My bowl had somehow slipped from front to back in my robe and was now supporting my weight between my shoulder blades. My barley bag—of hard leather—had worked down and was almost breaking my left ribs. Touchily I moved and stared up at the nine lamas sitting watching me. THEY were the horrible white blobs stuck on saffron streaks! I hoped that they did not know what I had thought.

"Yes, Lobsang, we DO know!" smiled one; "your telepathic thoughts were very clear on the subject. But rise slowly. You have done well and fully justified your Guide's remarks." Gingerly I sat up, receiving a hearty butt in the back and a roaring purr as I did so. The old cat came around to face me and touched my hand as a sign that he wanted his fur ruffled. Idly I did so as I collected my scattered wits and wondered what would happen next. "Well, Lobsang, that was a good experience of getting out of the body," said the lama who had accompanied me. "We must try it often so that you can get out of your body as easily as shrugging off your robe."

"But, Honorable Lama," I said in some confusion, "I did NOT leave my body—I took it with me!"

The lama-guide's jaw dropped in astonishment. "What DO you mean?" he exclaimed. "You travelled in spirit with me."

"Honorable Lama," was my rejoinder. "I looked specially, and my body was not on the floor, so I must have taken it with me."

The old, wizened lama, the smallest of the nine, smiled and said, "You are making a common mistake, Lobsang, for you are still bemused by the senses." I looked at him and quite honestly I did not know what he was talking about; it seemed to me that he had taken leave of HIS senses, for, I thought, surely I should know if I saw my own body or not, and if I did not see my body, then it must not have been there. I suppose they must have seen by my sceptical glance that I was not taking in what they were saying, what they were implying, because one of the other lamas motioned for me to pay attention.

"I am going to give you my version of it, Lobsang," said this other lama, "and I want you to pay close attention, for what I have to say is elementary, yet it is a matter which puzzles a lot of people. You were lying on the floor, and as this was your first conscious time of astral travelling we helped you, we helped ease your astral form out of your physical form, and because it was done by us who have a lifetime of experience you did not feel any jolt, or any disturbance. Therefore, it is clear that you had no idea that you were out of the body." I looked at him, and thought about it. I thought, yes, that is right, I had no idea that I was out of the body, no one had said that I was going to be out of the body, so if they hadn't told me what to expect, how could I have a feeling of leaving the body? But,

92

then, it all came back to me that I had looked down and I had not seen my body lying on the floor as surely I should have done unless I was still in the body. I shook my head as if to shake the cobwebs loose; I felt that all this was getting too deep for me. I was out of the body, yet my body wasn't there, so if it wasn't there where was it, and why hadn't I seen it lying about somewhere? Just then the old cat gave me another butt and started knitting, bumping up and down on my lap, sinking his claws into my robe, and purring louder and louder reminding me that I must stay aware of his presence also. The lama who had been speaking laughed as he remarked, "There! Old cat is telling you to scrape your brains clear so that you may perceive!"

I spread my fingers and raked the cat's back. His purrs increased in volume; then suddenly he just flopped at length. He was a big old thing, his head was sticking over one side of my lap and his legs were protruding over the other side, with his tail stretched straight out on the floor. These cats grew larger than the average sort of cat, they were normally fierce, but our temple cats all seemed to recognize me as a brother or something, because certainly I was as popular with them as they were with me.

The lama who had been speaking to me before turned to me saying, "Leave him be; he can rest on you while we talk to you. Perhaps he will give you a good dig every so often to remind you to pay attention. Now! People see what they expect to see. Often they do not see that which is most obvious. For instance," he looked hard at me as he said this, "how many cleaners were there in the corridor as you came along? Who was that man sweeping in the barley store? And if the Lord Abbot had sent for you and asked you to tell him if you had seen anyone in the inner corridor, what would you have told him?" He paused for a moment to see if I was going to make any remark, and as I stared at him—openmouthed, I am afraid—he continued, "You would have said you saw no one in the inner corridor because the person who was in the inner corridor was a person who has every right to be there, who is always there, and who would be so correct in that corridor that you would not even notice him. So—you would say you saw no one in that corridor."

Another lama broke in, nodding his head wisely as he added his piece; "The proctors often have some difficulty when they are carrying out an investigation; they may ask if there were any strangers, or if anyone had been in a certain building, and invariably a custodian of the building would say that, no, no one had been in. And yet there might have been a procession of people, there would be proctors passing, there would be perhaps a lama or two, and there might even be a messenger from another lamasery. But because these people were so common—that is, because it was so usual for them to be in the vicinity—their passage would pass unnoticed, and as far as being observed, they might just as well be invisible."

One who had not yet spoken nodded his head, "Yes, that is so. Now I ask you, Lobsang, how many times you have been in this temple? And yet by your look quite recently, you had not even seen the stand upon which we rested the crystal. That stand has been here for about two hundred years, it has not been out of this temple, and yet you looked at it as if you were seeing it for the first time. It was here before, but it was commonplace to you; therefore it was invisible."

The lama who had been with me on my astral trip through the Potala smiled as he continued: "You, Lobsang, had no idea of what was happening, you did not know you were going to be out of the body; therefore, you were not prepared to see your body. Thus, when you looked, you looked at lamas sitting in a circle, and your attention carefully avoided your own body. We get the same thing in hypnotism; we can hypnotize a person to make him believe that he is completely alone in a room, and then that person in a state of hypnosis will look everywhere in a room except at the person who shares the room with him, and the hypnotized person, on being awakened, would take an oath to the effect that he had been alone. In the same way, you carefully avoided looking at where your body was in plain view. Instead, you looked around the perimeter of the circle, you looked around the temple avoiding the one spot that you thought you wanted to see."

It really made me think; I had heard something like that before. I had once seen an old monk who had had a bad attack of migraine. As he had explained it to me afterwards, things at which he looked were not there, if he looked at a thing in front of him he could only see things at the side, but if he looked toward the side he could see things in front of him. He told me it was like looking through a pair of tubes placed over his eyes, so that in effect he was as one wearing blinkers.

A lama—I did not know one from the other then—said, "The obvious often might be invisible because the more common an object, the more familiar an object, the less noticeable it becomes. Take the man who brings barley: You see him every day, and yet you do not see him. He is such a familiar figure that had I asked you who came along here this morning you would say, no one, because you would not regard the barley-carrier as a person but just as something that always did a certain thing at a specified time."

It seemed most remarkable to me that I should be lying on the ground, but then be unable to see my own body. However, I had heard so much about hypnotism and astral travelling that I was quite able to accept their explanation.

The old, wizened lama smiled at me as he remarked, "We shall soon have to give you more specific instruction so that you can leave your body easily at any time. Like everyone else, you have been doing astral travelling every night, travelling off to distant places and then forgetting about it. But we want to show you how easy it is for you to get out of your body at any time at all, and go on an astral journey, and then return to your body retaining the full knowledge of all that you have seen, all that you have done. If you can do that, you can travel to the great cities of the world and you will not be isolated here in Tibet but can acquire a knowledge of all cultures."

I thought about that. I had wondered often how some of our higher lamas seemed to have all-knowledge, they seemed to be Beings apart, being remote from the pettiness of everyday life, being able to say what was happening at any moment in any part of our country—I remembered on one occasion I with my Guide had called upon an old, old man. I had been presented to him, and we had been talking, or rather my Guide and he had been talking and I had been respectfully listening. Suddenly the old man had held up his hand, saying, "I am called!" Then he had withdrawn, the light seemed to go out from his body. He sat there immobile, looking like a man dead, looking like an empty shell. My Guide sat quite still, and motioned for me also to be still and quiet. We sat together with our hands clasped in our laps, we sat without speaking, without moving. I watched what appeared to be the empty figure with vast interest; for perhaps ten, perhaps twenty minutes—it was difficult to gauge time under those circumstances—nothing happened. Then there was the color of animation returning to the old man. Eventually he stirred and opened his eyes, and then—I shall never forget it—he told my Guide exactly what was happening at Shigatse which was quite some way from us. It occurred to me that this was far better as a system of communication than all the remarkable devices I had heard of in the outside world.

I wanted to be able to astral travel anywhere. I wanted to be able to move across the mountains, and across the seas and into foreign lands. And these men, these nine lamas were going to teach me!

The old cat yawned, making his whiskers vibrate, and then he stood up and stretched and stretched until I almost thought he would break in two. Then he strolled off, arrogantly pushing his way between two lamas, and disappeared into the darkness behind one of the Sacred Figures. The old, wizened lama spoke, saying, "Well, it is time we brought this session to an end, for we did not come here to teach Lobsang on this occasion, this is just an incidental. We must set about our other work, and we will see Lobsang again when his Guide returns."

Another one turned to me and gave me a hard stare: "You will have to learn very carefully, Lobsang. You have a lot to do in life, you will have hardships, suffering, you will travel far and often. But in the end you will achieve that which is your task. We will give you the basic training." They rose to their feet, picked up the crystal leaving the stand, and left the temple.

I sat wondering. A task! Hardship? But I had always been told I had a hard life ahead of me, always been told I had a task, so why did they rub it in so? Anyhow, why did I have to do the task, why was I always the one to have suffering? The more I heard about it the less I liked it. But I did want to travel in the astral and see all the things I had heard about. Gingerly I climbed to my feet, wincing and muttering unkind words as the pains shot through my legs again. Pins and needles, and then a few bumps and bruises where I had fallen down a few times, and a pain between my shoulder blades where I had been resting upon my bowl. Thinking of that I reached inside my robe and sorted my possessions into their accustomed position. Then, with a final look around, I left the temple.

At the door I hastily turned and went back to the flickering butter lamps. One by one I snuffed them out, for that was my duty, I was the last one to leave, therefore I was the one to snuff out the lamps. As I felt my way through the darkness to where there was a faint glimmer from the open door, my nostrils were assailed by the stench of smoldering wicks. Somewhere off in a corner there was the dying red ember of a wick which was just then charring into blackness.

I stood for a moment at the door deciding which way I would go. Then, with my mind made up, I turned and made my way to the right. The bright starlight was pouring in through the windows, imparting a silvery-blue appearance to everything. I turned a corner in the corridor and stopped suddenly, thinking, yes, of course they were right. I stood there a moment and thought. It occurred to me that time after time I had passed an old monk sitting in a little cell, and yet although I saw him every day I had never even noticed him. I retraced my steps for perhaps ten yards, and peered in. There he was in a little stone cell on the far side of the corridor opposite the windows. He was blind, endlessly he sat there on the floor turning a Prayer Wheel—rather a big one, it was—turning, turning, turning. Whenever anyone passed by there was the eternal "click, click, click" of the old monk's Prayer Wheel. Hour after hour, day after day he sat there, believing that it was his allotted task in life to keep that Prayer Wheel turning, and that was all he lived for. We who passed that way so often were immune to the turning of the Wheel, we were so accustomed to it that we neither saw the old monk, nor heard his Wheel a-click.

I stood there in the dark doorway and pondered as the Wheel clicked on, and as the old man softly droned, "Om! Mani padmi hum! Om! Mani padmi hum!" His voice was hoarse, and his fingers were twisted and gnarled. I could make him out but dimly and he was quite oblivious of me, turning the Wheel, turning the Wheel, as he had turned the Wheel for so many years, turning it long before I was born. How much longer will he turn it? I wondered. But it pointed out to me that people were invisible if they were so familiar that one did not have to notice them. It occurred to me, too, that sounds were silences if one became too accustomed to them.

I thought of the times when I had been quite alone in a dark cell, and then after a time I would hear the gurgle and rustle of body sounds, the blood surging through the veins and arteries of the body, and then I would hear the steady thud, thud, thud of my heart pumping away. After a time, too, I could actually hear the air sighing through my lungs, and when I moved the slight creak and snap of muscles pulling bones to a different position. We all have that, we are all noisy contraptions, I thought, and yet when there are other sounds which attract our attention we just do not hear those with which we are constantly surrounded and which do not obtrude.

I stood on one leg, and scratched my head. Then I thought the night was already far advanced, soon there would come the call to temple service at midnight. So I hesitated no more but put both feet on the ground, pulled my robe more tightly around me, and moved off up the corridor to the dormitory. As soon as I lay down I fell asleep.

Sleep was not long my companion; I twisted and turned, creaked and groaned as I lay and thought of life as it was in a lamasery. About me boys wheezed and muttered in their sleep, the sound of their snores rising and falling on the night air. One boy who suffered from adenoids was making a "globble-globble, globble-globble" until in desperation I rose and turned him on his side. I lay on my back, thinking, listening. From somewhere came the monotonous click-click of a Prayer Wheel as some monk endlessly twirled it so that his prayers could go winging forth. From afar came the muted clop-clop as someone rode a horse up the path outside our window. The night dragged on. Time stood still. Life was an eternity of waiting, waiting, where nothing moved, where all was still save for the snores, the click of the Prayer Wheel and the muffled steps of the horse. I must have dozed.

Wearily I sat up. The floor was hard and unyielding. The cold of the stone was creeping into my bones. Somewhere a boy muttered that he wanted his mother. Stiffly I climbed to my feet and moved to the window, carefully avoiding the sleeping bodies around me. The cold was intense and there was a threat of snow to come. Over the vast Himalayan ranges the morning was sending forth tendrils of light, colored fingers seeking our Valley, waiting to light up another day.

The spume of snow-dust always flying from the very highest peaks was illumined now by golden light shining on its underside, while from the top came scintillating rainbow crescents which wavered and blossomed to the vagaries of the high winds. Across the sky shot vivid beams of light as the sun peeped through the mountain passes and gave a promise of another day soon to be. The stars faded. No longer was the sky a purple vault; it lightened, lightened, and became the palest blue. The whole of the mountains were limned with gold as the sky grew brighter. Gradually the blinding orb of the sun climbed above the mountain passes and shone forth in blazing glory into our Valley.

The cold was intense. Ice crystals fell from the sky and cracked on the roof with a musical tinkle. There was a bitterness, a sharpness in the air that almost froze the marrow in one's bones. What a peculiar climate, I thought, sometimes too cold to snow, and yet—sometimes at midday it would be uncomfortably hot. Then, in the twinkling of an eye, a great wind storm would rise and send all flying before it. Always, in the mountains, there was snow, deep snow, but on the exposed stretches the winds blew away the snow as fast as it fell. Our country was high, and with rarefied air. Air so thin and clear that it afforded scant shelter from the ultraviolet (or heat generating) rays of the sun. In our summer a monk could swelter miserably in his robes, then, as a cloud momentarily obscured the sun, the temperature would fall to many degrees below freezing—all in a few minutes.

We suffered greatly from wind storms. The great barrier of the Himalayas sometimes held back clouds that formed over India, causing a temperature inversion. Then howling gales would pour over the mountain lips and storm down into our Valley, sweeping all before it. People who wandered abroad during the storms had to wear leather face-masks or risk having the skin stripped from them by the rock-dust torrenting down, wind-borne, from the highest reaches. Travellers caught in the open, on the mountain passes, would risk being blown away; unless they were alert and quick to act, their tents and other possessions would be blown into the air, whirling ragged and ruined, playthings of the mindless wind.

Somewhere below, in the pale morning a yak bellowed mournfully. As if at the signal, the trumpets blared forth from the roof high above. The conches lowed and throbbed, to echo and re-echo and fuse into a medley of sound like some multiple chord played on a mighty organ. About me there were all the myriad sounds of a large community awakening to a new day, to another day of life. A chant from the Temple, the neighing of horses, muttered grumbles from sleepy small boys shivering naked in the intensely cold air. And as a muted undertone, the incessant clicking of the Prayer Wheels located throughout the buildings, turned and turned eternally by old, old monks who thought that that was their sole purpose in life.

The place was astir. Activity increased from moment to moment. Shaven heads peered hopefully from open windows, wishing for a warmer day. A dark blob, shapeless, formless, wobbled from somewhere above and crossed my line of vision to crash with a sharp crack on the rocks below. Someone's bowl, I thought, now HE will have to go without breakfast until he can obtain another! Breakfast? Of course! We have started another day, a day when I would need to have my strength up because I was hoping that my beloved Guide would be returning this day, and before I could see him there were morning classes, temple service—but before all—BREAKFAST!

Tsampa is unappetizing stuff, but it was all I knew about except for very rare, very infrequent delicacies from India. So I trudged off down the corridor, following the line of boys and monks wending their way down to the hall where we ate.

At the entrance I hung around a bit, waiting for some of the others to settle down because I was shaky on my legs, somewhat uncertain of my steps, and when everyone was milling about it posed a definite threat to my stability. Eventually I walked in and took my place among the lines of men and boys sitting on the floor. We sat cross-legged (all except me, and I sat with my legs tucked under me). There were lines of us, perhaps two hundred and fifty of us at one time. As we sat there monk attendants came and ladled out tsampa, passing along the rows, giving each of us our fair, equitable share. Monks stood at the sides of each row, and then at a given signal they all went between our ranks with our food. No one could eat, though, until the Attending Master gave the signal. At last each monk and boy had his bowl full of tsampa; the attendants stood at the side.

An old lama walked to the lectern, a lectern raised up high above us so that he could look down on us. He stood there and lifted the top sheet off his book, for our pages, remember, were long things not bound together as is the Western style. This lama lifted off the top sheet, and then signalled that he was ready to start. Immediately the Attending Master raised his hand and brought it down as a signal for us to start our meal. As we did so the Lector commenced his reading from the Sacred Books, his voice droning on and on, seeming to echo around the place, and making much of what he said unintelligible.

Around the dining hall the ever-present Proctors padded silently, making no sound save for the occasional swish of their robes.

In the lamaseries throughout Tibet it was the fixed custom that a Lector should read to us while we ate because it was considered wrong for a person to eat and think of food; food was a gross thing, merely necessary to sustain the body so that it could for a little while be inhabited by an immortal spirit. So, although it was necessary to eat, yet we were not supposed to get pleasure from it. The Lector read to us always from Sacred Books, so that while our bodies had food for the body, our spirit had food for the soul.

The senior lamas always ate alone, most times thinking of some sacred text or looking at some sacred object or book. It was a very great offence to talk while eating, and any unlucky wretch caught talking was hauled forth by the Proctors and made to lie across the doorway so that when everyone left, they had to step across the recumbent figure, and that brought much shame to the victim.

We boys were always the first to finish, but then we had to keep quiet until all the others had finished. Often the Lector would go on reading quite oblivious of the fact that everyone was waiting for him. Often we would be made late for classes because the Lector, getting absorbed in his subject, would forget time and place.

At last the Lector finished his page and looked up with some start of surprise, and then half turned to the next page. But, instead, he put the cover on the book, and tied the tapes together; lifting the book off he handed it to a monk-attendant who took it, bowed, and removed the book for safe keeping. The Attending Master then gave the signal for us to dismiss. We went to the side of the hall where there were leather bags of fine sand, and with a handful of sand we cleaned out our eating bowls, the only utensil we had because, of course, we used our fingers—the oldest utensil of all!—and had no use for knives and forks.

"Lobsang! Lobsang! Go down to the Master of the Paper and get me three sheets which can be spoiled on one side." A young lama stood before me, giving me the order. I muttered grumpily and stumped off down the corridor. This was one of the types of jobs I hated, because for this particular thing I would have to get out of the Potala and go all the way down to the Village of Shö, where I would have to see the Master Printer and get the paper desired.

Paper is very rare, very expensive in Tibet. It is, of course, absolutely handmade. Paper is treated as a minor religious object, because nearly always it was used for sacred knowledge, sacred words, thus paper was never abused and never thrown away. If in printing a book the print was smeared, the paper was not scrapped but the unspoiled side was available for teaching us. There was always a plentiful supply of spoiled paper for such purposes because we printed from hand-carved wooden blocks, and of course a block had to be carved in reverse so that it could print the right way. Thus, in trying out the blocks, there were inevitably many sheets of paper spoiled.

I made my way out of the Potala, going down by the lower back entrance where the way was very steep but much shorter, and where there were no steps to tire my legs. Here by the lower back entrance we would go down, lowering ourselves from bush to bush, or if we missed our footing we would skate down on a cloud of dust and wear a great hole in the seat of our robes, a matter which was difficult to explain later.

I went down the narrow, narrow path with the overhanging bushes. At a small clearing I stopped and peered out, peered out in the direction of Lhasa hoping to see a very special saffron robe coming across the Turquoise Bridge, or possibly—what joy the thought brought!—coming along the Ring Road. But no, there were only the pilgrims, only the stray monks and an ordinary lama or two. So, with a sigh and a grunt of disgust, I continued my slithering path downward.

At last I arrived down by the Courts of Justice and made my way around to the Printing Office. Inside there was an old, old monk; he seemed to be all smeared with ink, and his thumb and forefingers were absolutely spatulate from handling paper and printing blocks.

I went and looked about, for the smell of the paper and the ink always fascinated me. I looked at some of the intricately carved wooden boards which were going to be used for printing new books, and I rather looked forward to the time when I should be able to take a hand at carving because it was quite a hobby of mine, and we monks were always given opportunities of displaying our skills for the good of the community.

"Well, boy, well! What do you want? Quick, what is it?" The old printer-monk was looking at me severely, but I knew him of old, his bark was definitely worse than his bite; in fact, he was rather a nice old man who was merely scared that small boys were going to crumple precious sheets of paper. Quickly I gave my message to the effect that I wanted three sheets of paper. He grunted in reply, turned away and peered, and peered, and peered, and looked as if he could not bear to give away his loved pieces of paper. He looked at each sheet, and kept on changing his mind. In the end I got tired of it and picked up three sheets saying, "Thank you, Honorable Printer, I have these three sheets, they will do."

He spun around and looked at me with his mouth wide open, a picture of stupefaction. By that time I had reached the door, complete with three sheets, and when he recovered his wits enough to say anything I was out of hearing.

Carefully I rolled the three sheets so the spoiled surface was outside. Then I tucked it into the front of my robe, and made my way up again, pulling myself hand over hand by the hardy bushes.

At the clearing I stopped again; officially it would have been to regain my breath, but actually I sat on a rock and looked for some time in the direction of Sera, the Wild Rose Fence. But no, there was just the ordinary traffic, nothing more. Possibly a few more traders than usual, but not the one that I desired to see.

At last I got to my feet and continued my journey upward, going again through the little door, and searching for the young lama who had sent me.

He was in a room by himself, and I saw that he was composing. Silently I held out the three sheets to him, and he said, "Oh! You have been a long time. Have you been making the paper?" He took them without further word, and without a word of thanks. So I turned and left him, and made my way up to the classrooms, thinking that I would have to fill in the day somehow until my Guide returned.

CHAPTER NINE

I STOOD on the storehouse roof, standing high above the surrounding ground. Before me stretched the whole of the Valley of Lhasa, green and beautiful, with the colored houses and the blue of the Turquoise Bridge. Farther, the golden roof of the Cathedral of Lhasa gleamed brightly, standing erect as it had stood for centuries, weathering the storms. Behind me, although at this time I did not turn my head, was the Happy River, and beyond the towering range of mountains with the passes leading up, ever higher, and descending through great gorges, great canyons, until one could turn one's head and see the last of Lhasa. Then straighten up and carry on in the direction of India, and to see part of Nepal, part of Sikkim, and part of India stretched out in front. But that was commonplace to me, I knew all about it. My whole attention now was riveted on the City of Lhasa.

Below me to the right, or rather, almost directly below me, was the Western Gate, the entrance to the City, thronged as ever with beggars crying for alms, pilgrims hoping for a blessing from the Holy One, and traders. As I stood there, shading my eyes against the harsh light so that I could see more clearly, the rising voices carried their messages to me: "Alms! Alms for the love of the Holy One! Alms that you in your hour of distress may be given aid too!" Then from another direction, "Oh! This is a real bargain, ten rupees only, ten Indian rupees and you have this precious bargain; you will never see the like of it again for our times change. Or I'll tell you what—you've been a good customer, let us make it nine rupees. You give me nine rupees now, and I will pass this over to you and we part good friends!"

From the Ring Road just below, the pilgrims were going along, some stretching their length, rising and stretching their length again, as if that peculiar form of locomotion would give them some salvation. But others walked erect, gazing at the rock carvings, the colored rock carvings which were one of the beautiful features of this mountain. As they came into sight I could hear them muttering, "Oh, there is someone on the roof there staring out. Do you think it is a lama?" The thought almost made me laugh. I, a small boy, standing aloft with the wind fluttering through my ragged robes. I, a lama? No, not yet, but I would be in time.

The pilgrims muttered away at their eternal "Om mani padme! Hum!" The traders tried to sell them charms, Prayer Wheels, amulets, and horoscopes. Most of the horoscopes, the charms, and the amulets had been made in India and imported, but the pilgrims would not know that, nor would they know that none of these things had been blessed in the manner promised. But does it not happen in all countries, in all religions? Are not traders the same everywhere?

I stared out from my lofty perch, staring out in the direction of Lhasa, staring out trying to penetrate the light haze which was formed by the yak-dung fires being lit to warm the houses, for a nip was coming in the air. The weather was definitely worsening. I looked up at the snow-laden clouds racing overhead, and I shivered. Sometimes it was remarkably hot, perhaps forty degrees fahrenheit, at this time of the day, but then by night it would drop far below freezing. But not even the weather was of much concern to me at this particular moment.

I eased myself, trying to support some of my weight on my elbows which I rested on the wall in front of me, and I stared and stared until my eyes ached, and until I imagined that I saw that which I desired. At one time I started up in high excitement; a lama in a scintillating saffron robe was coming into sight. I started up in such excitement that my treacherously weak legs betrayed me, and I toppled back knocking the wind from me, and making me gasp for seconds before I could scramble to my feet again and peer on, on in the direction of Lhasa. But no, the wearer of the saffron robe was not the lama whom I sought. I watched him riding along with his attendants, watched him enter the Ring Road there, and saw the pilgrims make way for him, and bow in his direction as he passed. Then after half an hour or so he came up the path before me, as he did so he looked up and saw me and made motions with his hands which I correctly understood to mean that my Guide would be coming shortly.

This was a kindness, and a kindness which I greatly appreciated because high lamas were not much in the habit of paying attention to small boys, but as I already had good reason to know there were lamas AND lamas—some were remote, completely austere, withdrawn from the emotions of life, while others were jolly, always ready to help another no matter his rank, or age, or station in life, and who was to say which one was the better, the austere or the compassionate. My choice was the compassionate man who could understand the miseries and the sufferings of small boys.

From a higher window, a window which I could not reach because I was just an acolyte, a head protruded and looked down. The face had a moustache. I bowed my head reverently, and when I looked again the face had vanished. For a moment or two I stood in contemplation, hoping that I had not caused annoyance by climbing up here onto this roof. And as far as I knew, I was not breaking any rules, this time I was trying desperately hard to behave and not do anything which could cause me to be delayed in seeing my Guide when he returned.

Over at the slightly higher Chakpori I could see monks going about their business; they seemed to be going in procession around the walls, and I thought that no doubt they were giving thanks that another batch of herbs had arrived from the highlands where they grew. I knew that a party of monks had recently arrived from the annual herb-gathering in the highlands, and I hoped that before too long I would be a member of such parties.

From afar off there came a trail of smoke. I could see a small group of men milling about, presumably they were brewing their tea so they could make tsampa. Traders, that was clear, for there was no colored robe among them, just the drab colors of traders, and these all wore their fur hats.

The chill wind was growing once again. Down below traders were gathering up their goods and scurrying for shelter. The pilgrims were crouching on the lee-side of the mountain, and the beggars were showing remarkable agility, some, in fact, even forgot their pretended illnesses as they hurried to get away from the approaching sand storm, or rather, dust storm.

The Valley of Lhasa was habitually swept clean by the gales which swept down from the mountains, blowing everything before them. Only the larger stones remained in place. Dust, grit, sand, all were swept away. But with every high wind, fresh sand and dust came upon us, sand borne by great boulders which had been rocking and swaying in the mountains, and then perhaps had collided with some other rock and shattered, forming pulverised stone which, becoming wind-borne, swept down upon us.

The wind so suddenly having arisen pressed hard against my back, plastering my robe tightly to the stone wall in front of me, pressing so hard that I could not move. Grimly I clung to the wall, trying to find finger holds, trying to let myself sink down so that I should be a bundle on the roof and thus afford the wind little grip for it to lift me. Painfully I let my knees fold, with infinite caution I lowered myself down so that I formed just a tight ball with my face and head protected from the stone-laden gale.

For minutes the wind howled and shrieked, and seemed to threaten to blow away the mountain itself. The wind howled louder than our trumpets ever blared, and then on the instant, remarkably, strangely, there came complete silence, a dead calm. In the silence I heard a sudden laugh, a girl's laugh from somewhere in the bushes below. "Oh!" she said. "Not here in this Holy place, that is sacrilege." Then a giggle, and a young man and a girl sauntered into view, hand in hand, as they crossed toward the Western Gate. I watched them idly for a few moments, then they strolled out of sight and out of my life.

I stood, and stared and stared again, over the tops of the trees along in the direction of Lhasa. But the storm had left us and it was now at Lhasa. The view was blanked out, all I saw was a great cloud like a grey blanket held to intercept the view. The cloud was featureless, but it was travelling rapidly, it gave one the impression of two Gods, each holding the end of a grey blanket, and running with it. As I watched more and more buildings became visible, and the cloud went on receding rapidly down the Valley, becoming smaller and smaller as it did, as the wind forces became spent and the heavier particles of dust and grit fell.

But I was watching in the direction of Lhasa, not a silly dust cloud which I could see at any time. I rubbed my eyes and stared again. I tried to force myself to see more than was really there, but in the end I saw a small party of men just appearing beyond some buildings. Some of them were wearing saffron robes. They were too far away for me to see individuals, but I knew—I knew!

I watched enthralled, and with my heart beating more rapidly than was its wont. The little group of men rode on sedately, not hurrying, an orderly procession. Gradually they approached the entrance of the Turquoise Bridge, and then were concealed from my gaze by that beautiful enclosed structure until they appeared again at the near end.

I stared and stared, trying to imagine which was which. Gradually, with painful slowness, they came closer and closer. My heart leaped within me as at last I could recognize the one saffron robe in which I was interested. I tried to dance with joy on the roof, but my legs would not permit me, so I braced my arms against the wall again in an unsuccessful attempt to control the trembling of my limbs, trembling more from excitement than from weakness on this occasion.

The little cavalcade drew closer and closer, until at last they were hidden from me by the larger buildings of the Village of Shö beneath. I could hear the clattter of the horses' hooves, I could hear the rustle and grate of harness and the occasional squeak of a leather bag being pressed perhaps between rider and horse.

I stood on tiptoe and tried to make myself taller so that I could see more. As I peered over the edge I could just make out heads wending their slow way up the stepped path toward the main entrance. Briefly one in the saffron robe looked up, smiled, and waved his hand. I was too overcome to wave back. I stood there and stared, and trembled with relief that soon he would be with me again.

A word was said to another lama, and he, too, looked up and smiled. This time I was able to force my features into a rather trembly sort of smile in return, because I was overcome with emotion, I could feel emotion welling up inside me, and I was desperately afraid that I was going to break down and prove that I was not a man.

The little cavalcade mounted higher and higher, making for the main entrance to the Potala, as was right for such an august party. Now, as I well knew, there would be a little delay because my Guide would have first to go to the Inmost One and make his report, and then he would in the fullness of time make his way to his own rooms in the higher portion of the Potala, whence, after a suitable interval, he would send a boy in search of me.

I slithered down from my post and dusted my hands and knees, and tried to make sure that my robe was fairly presentable. Then I made my way to the little house on the roof, entered, it, and very carefully and slowly climbed down the ladder to the floor below. I had to make sure that I was available whenever a messenger came in search of me, and I wanted first of all to make sure that I was as tidy as I could make myself.

Our ladders were rather hazardous contraptions for anyone who had any leg troubles. They consisted of a substantial pole, well smoothed, and with notches cut on each side so that one put one leg—or rather, one foot—on the left side, and then one put the right foot to a higher notch on the right side, and one climbed up in that manner with the pole between one's knees. If one was not careful, or the pole was loose, one would slip around to the wrong side, often to the great glee of small boys. A menace of which one had to be wary was that often the pole-ladders would be slippery with butter because when one climbed a pole with a butter lamp in the hand, often the butter which had melted would slop and add to one's problems. But this was not a time to think of ladders or butter lamps. I reached the floor, carefully dusted myself off again, and scraped off a few dabs of congealed butter. Then I made my way into the boys' part of the building.

In our dormitory I walked impatiently to the window and peered out, kicking my heels against the wall as a sign of my impatience. I peered out, this time out of sheer boredom, for there was nothing I wanted to see outside, the one I wanted to see was inside!

In Tibet we did not use mirrors—not officially, that is, because mirrors were considered a vanity; if any person was caught looking in a mirror it was considered that he was thinking more of carnal things than of spiritual things. It was a great help in keeping to this attitude that we had no mirrors! On this particular occasion, however, I urgently desired to see what I looked like, and so I made my way surreptitiously into one of the temples where there was a very shiny copper plate. It was so shiny that after I had rubbed the hem of my robe across it a few times I was able to look into the surface and get an idea of what I looked like. Having looked hard, and long, and feeling heartily discouraged at what I saw, I put back the plate and made my way in search of the barber-monk, for I was looking like a "Black Head."

In Tibet "Black Heads" are people who are not in Holy Orders. Monks and all those coming under acolyte, trappa, monk, or monastic orders, shaved their heads, and so they were frequently known as "Red Heads" because that is what we had when the sun did its worst. On the other hand, lay people had their heads covered with black hair, and so they were known as "Black Heads." It should be added here that we also referred to "Saffron Robes" when we meant the higher lamas; we never said "the wearer of the saffron robe," but only "Saffron Robes." In the same way, we talked of "Red Robes" or "Grey Robes" because to us the robe was the thing, as indicating the status of the person inside it. It was also clear to us by Tibetan logic that there must be a person inside the robe, or the robe would not be able to move about!

I made my way deeper and deeper along the sloping corridors of the Potala, and then at last I approached the rather big room where the barber-monk plied his trade. He was one who was called a monk by courtesy because it seemed to me that he never left his particular room, and certainly never attended services. I strolled along the corridor and entered his door. As usual the place was filled with hangers-on, shiftless monks who hung about, the barber-monk, the kitchen-monks, in fact, anywhere where they could skulk and just waste their own and somebody else's time. But today there was quite an excited air about the place, and I looked to see the reason.

On a low bench there was a pile of remarkably tattered and torn magazines. Apparently one of the monks had done some service for a group of traders, and the traders out of the kindness of their hearts had given him a whole load of magazines and papers which they had brought for various purposes from India. Now there was quite a throng of monks in the barber-monk's room, and they were waiting for another monk who had spent some time in India and thus could be presumed to understand what was in the magazines.

Two monks were laughing and chattering over some picture in a magazine. One said to the other, laughingly, "We must ask Lobsang about all this; he should be a specialist on such things. Come here, Lobsang!" I went over to where they were sitting on the floor looking at pictures. I took the magazine from them, and then one said, "But, look, you have the magazine upside-down; you don't even know which way to hold the thing." Unfortunately, to my shame, I found that he was right. I sat down between them and looked at the most remarkable picture. It was of a brownish color, sepia, I think the correct term would be, and it depicted a strange-looking woman. She was sitting on a high table in front of a bigger table, and on a framed affair on the bigger table there was a picture, or reflection of the woman.

Her dress really intrigued me because it seemed to be longer than a monk's robe. She had a remarkably small waist which appeared to be belted tightly to make it even smaller yet her arms were heavily padded, and when I looked at her chest I found myself blushing with embarrassment because her dress was remarkably low—dangerously low, I should say—and I found to my shame that I wondered what would happen if she bent forward. But in this picture she was keeping a rigidly straight back.

As we sat there looking at the picture another monk came in and stood behind us; we took no notice of him. One of the people milling around said, "Whatever is she doing?" The monk who had just entered bent down and read what was written beneath, and then he said grandly, "Oh, she is merely making-up her face, she is applying lipstick, and when she has done that she will use eyebrow pencil. That is a cosmetic advertisement." All this confused me beyond belief. Making-up her face? Putting on lipstick? Putting on eyebrow pencil?

I turned to the English-reading monk behind me, and said, "But why does she want to mark where her mouth is? Doesn't she know?" He laughed at me, and said, "Some of these people, they put red or orange around their lips, it is supposed to make them more attractive. And when they have done that they do things to their eyebrows and perhaps to their eyelids.

And when they have finished with that lot, they go and put dust on their faces, dust of various colors." All this seemed very strange to me, and I said, "But why hasn't she got her dress on covering the top part of her body?" Everyone laughed at me, but everyone took a jolly good look to see what I was getting at. The English-reading monk laughed loudest of all, and said, "If you see these Westerners at their parties you will find that they wear very little on their chest, but a very great deal below the waist!"

I pored over the pictures, trying to understand what they were all about. I did not see how the woman could move about in such uncomfortable clothes. She appeared to have no feet, but the cloth went all the way down to the ground and trailed behind her. But I soon forgot all about that when I heard the English-reading monk telling others about the magazines.

"Look at this one, the date says 1915, there's a very great war on in the West and it's going to envelop the whole world. People are fighting, killing each other, and they dig holes in the ground and they stay in those holes, and when the rains come they nearly drown."

"What is the war about?" asked another monk. "Oh, never mind what the war is about; Western people don't need any reason to fight, they just fight." He turned over a few magazines, then he came to another. It showed a most remarkable thing, it seemed to be a great iron box, and according to the picture it was running over the ground running over soldiers who were trying to escape. "That," said the English-reading monk, "is the latest invention; it is called a tank, and it might be a thing which will win the war."

We looked, and we thought about the war, we thought of all the souls getting injured when their physical bodies were destroyed. I thought of how many sticks of incense would have to be burned to help all those wandering souls.

"The British are raising another battalion of Gurkhas, I see," said the monk who read English. "But they never think of asking for any spiritual assistance from Tibet." I was rather glad they did not because I could not see any sense in all the killing, all the bloodshed, all the suffering. It seemed so stupid to me that grown men had to squabble and come to blows just because one set of people could not agree with another set of people. I sighed and shook my head in considerable exasperation to think that it was my unfortunate destiny to travel to the Western world later. All that had been foreordained, my future had been told to me with extreme clarity, but I did not like any of the things that had been told to me, it entailed too much suffering, too much hardship!

"Lobsang!" a voice bawled at me. I looked up; there was the monk-barber motioning for me to come and sit on his three-legged stool. I did so, and he stood behind me and picked up the huge blade with which he shaved our heads. He did not use soap or water, of course, he just made a few strokes with the razor blade across a piece of stone, and then grabbing my temples firmly with his left hand he began the painful process of scraping off the stubble from my skull. None of us liked this process, and we all expected to end up with a bloody head—with a head nicked, chopped, and gashed. However, Tibetans are not soft, they do not run screaming at the first trace of pain. So I sat there while the monk-barber scraped and scraped away. "I suppose I'd better trim your neck, eh?" he said. "Understand your Guide man has returned—you'll be wanting to rush off, eh?" With that he shoved my head down almost between my knees, and then scraped industriously at the long hair where my head joined my neck. All the time he kept blowing at me, blowing off the hair which he had cut, and each time (if I guessed the right time!) I held my breath because his breath was—well—not pleasant, apparently his teeth were rotting or something. At last, though, he finished his scraping and we started to mop up the blood from the numerous scratches. Someone said, "Quickest way to stop it is to put a piece of paper on each scratch. Let's try it." So I ended looking something like a scarecrow with little three-cornered bits of paper stuck to bloody patches.

I had nothing better to do for a time, so I stayed in the barber-monk's room and listened to all the conversation. It seemed that matters were in a very bad state in the Western world, it seemed that the world was just about aflame. There seemed to be trouble in Russia, trouble in England, the Irish people were making a commotion—only we of Tibet were peaceful. I fell silent as I recalled the prophecies which had been made about Tibet centuries before, and I knew that in our time, in my lifetime in fact, we of Tibet would have our own troubles. I knew also that our own beloved Dalai Lama would be the last actual Dalai Lama, and although there would be one more, he would not be of the same spiritual significance.

Idly I turned over a page and saw a most extraordinary picture; it seemed to consist of a lot of boxes with pieces cut out of the sides, and out of the sides people's faces were peering. The boxes were all joined together, and they seemed to be drawn along by some monster which was belching smoke. There were circular things beneath the boxes, and there seemed to be two lines between them. I could not at all make out the significance of what it was, I did not at that time know that they were wheels, and what I was seeing was a train, because in Tibet the only wheels were Prayer Wheels. I turned to the English-reading monk and tugged at his robe. Eventually he turned to me, and I asked him to tell me what it said. He translated for me that it was a British troop train taking soldiers to fight in the fields of Flanders.

Another picture fascinated me and thrilled me beyond all explanation; it was of a contraption that appeared to be a kite with no string keeping it in touch with the ground. This kite seemed to be a framework covered with cloth, and in the front of it there seemed to be a thing which, by the representation of the picture, must have been revolving, and I saw there were two people in this kite, one in the front and one sitting close behind. The quite friendly English-reading monk told me that it was an airplane, a thing that I had never heard of before. I resolved that if I were ever

117

expelled from the lamasery, or from the Order, I would not be a boatman, but I would instead be one of those people who flew those strange kites which they had in the West. And then, as I turned those pages I saw another thing, a thing which frightened me speechless for a time—and that was a feat in itself—for this thing appeared to be a long tube covered with cloth or some sort of material, and it was shown as if flying above a city and dropping great black things on the city. Other pictures showed the black things landing, and showed a flash and damage as buildings flew up in the air. The monk told me that it was a thing called a zeppelin which was used to bomb England, and that a bomb was a metal cannister filled with high explosive which blew everything from its path when it landed. It seemed to me that these magazines had nothing of peace in them, they were, instead, dealing only with war. I thought that I had looked enough at those pictures which merely served to inflame men's angry passions, and so I put down the magazines, made my thanks to the English-reading monk and to the barber-monk, and made my way upwards again to the dormitory where I knew I could soon expect a messenger.

The endless day drew on. Once again it was time for tsampa. I went down into the hall and had my meal with the others, but I confess the day was endless, endless. I had little appetite, but I thought I should take the advantage and eat while there was still time.

Having cleaned my bowl I left the dining hall, made my way up again to the dormitory, and stood for a time looking out of the window, watching the bustle that surrounded our buildings.

CHAPTER TEN

SOON THERE came to our corridor a boy yelling "LOBSANG! LOBSANG!" I hastened across the room and met him at the door as he was about to enter. "Phew!" he exclaimed, wiping imaginary perspiration from his brow, "I've looked EVERYWHERE for you. Been in hiding or something? Your Guide wants you."

"What does he look like?" I asked, in some anxiety.

"Look like? LOOK like? What do you you expect him to look like? You saw him just a few day ago, what's wrong with you, anyhow, sick or something?" The boy wandered off muttering about stupid. . . . I turned away and pulled my robe straight and felt to be sure that my bowl and charm box were in place. Then I walked up the corridor.

It was a pleasure to leave the Boys' Quarters, with the smeared lime-washed walls, and enter the much more ornate Lamas' Quarters. As I wandered softly along I could see into most of the rooms I passed; most of the lamas kept their doors open. Here an old man was fingering his beads and reciting endlessly, "Om! Mani padme Hum!" Another was reverently turning the pages of some old, old book, looking unceasingly for yet another meaning from the Scriptures. It rather bothered me to see these old men trying to read "between the lines"—trying to read into writing those messages which were not put there in the first place. Then they would burst out with, "A New Interpretation of the Scriptures, by Lama so-and-so." A very ancient man, with a straggly, white beard, was gently twirling a Prayer Wheel and crooning to himself as he did so. Yet another was declaiming to himself—practicing for a forthcoming theological debate in which he was to take a leading part.

"Now don't you come here leaving dirt on my clean floor, you young squirt!" said a testy old cleaning-monk, as he leaned on his brush and eyed me baleful-ly. "I don't work here all day for the likes of you!"

"Go and jump out of the window, old one!" I said rudely as I walked past him. He stretched out and tried to grab me, but, tripping over his long brush handle, fell to the floor with a resounding thud. I hastened my steps so as to have a head start before he could climb to his feet. No one took any notice; Prayer Wheels still hummed and clacked, the Declaimer still declaimed, and voices still intoned their mantras.

In some near room an old man was hawking and clearing his throat with horrid noises. "Hrruk! Hrruk! Uahha!" he went in his endless attempt to obtain relief. I walked on. These corridors were long and I had to walk from the quarters of the lowest form of lamastic life to almost the highest—to that of the very senior lamas. Now, as I progressed towards the "better" area, more doors were shut. At last I turned off the main corridor and entered a small annex, the domain of "The Special Ones." Here, in the place of honor, my Guide resided when at the Potala.

With a rapidly beating heart I stopped at a door and knocked. "Come in!" said a well-loved voice. I entered and made my ritual bows to the shining personage sitting with his back to the window. The Lama Mingyar Dondup smiled kindly at me and very carefully looked at me to see how I had fared during the past seven or so days. "Sit down, Lobsang, sit down!" he said, point-ing to a cushion placed before him. For some time we sat while he asked me questions—most difficult to answer, some of them were, too! This great man filled me with the deepest feelings of love and devotion; I wanted nothing more than to be continually in his presence.

"The Inmost One is very pleased with you," he remarked, adding idly, "and I suppose that calls for some sort of celebration." He stretched out his hand and tinkled his small silver bell. A serving-monk entered and brought a low table, one of those ornate things carved and with many coats of color. I was always afraid of scratching or marking the wretched things. The table was placed to the right of my Guide. Smiling at me, the Lama turned to the serving-monk and said, "You have the plain table ready for Lobsang?"

"Yes, Master," the man replied. "I will fetch it now." He left, soon returning with a very plain table which had the best "ornaments" of all; it was laden with things from India. Sweet and sticky cakes which were covered with some sort of syrup which had then been sprinkled with sugar, pickled walnuts, special chestnuts which had been brought from a far, far country, and many other items which delighted my heart. The serving-monk smiled slightly as he also put beside me a large jar of the herbs which we used when afflicted with indigestion.

Another serving-monk entered bearing small cups and a large jug full of steaming Indian tea. At a sign from my Guide they withdrew, and I had a pleasant change from tsampa! I did not bother to think about the other acolytes who probably never in their lives had tasted anything except tsampa. I knew quite well that probably tsampa would be their only food for as long as they lived, and I consoled myself with the thought that if they suddenly had a taste of these exotic foods from India it would make them dissatisfied. I knew that I was going to have a hard time in life, I knew that soon there would be very different foods for me, so in my small-boy smug complacency I thought there was nothing wrong in having a foretaste of pleasant things to compensate for the unpleasant things which I had already endured. So I ate more than I should have with complete tranquillity. My Guide remained silent, and all he had was tea—the Indian variety. But eventually, with a sigh of the utmost regret, I decided that I could not take even another crumb; in fact, the mere sight of that wretched food was beginning to appear distasteful to me, it was coloring my outlook, and I felt—well—as if enemies were fighting inside me. I became aware that certain strange specks were floating before my eyes, so I had no more to eat, and before long I had to withdraw to another place, for the food had stretched my stomach rather painfully!

When I returned, somewhat paler, considerably lighter, and a little shaken, my Guide was still sitting, still unruffled, quite benign. He smiled at me as I settled myself again, saying, "Well! Now you have had and lost most of your tea, you at least have the memory of it, and that might help you. We will talk about various things." I settled myself very comfortably. His eyes were roaming, no doubt wondering how my injuries were, then he told me: "I had a talk with the Inmost One who told me of your, er—flying onto the Golden Roof. His Holiness told me all about it, told me what he had seen, and told me that you risked expulsion to tell him the truth. He is very pleased with you, very pleased with the reports he has had about you, very pleased with what he has seen, for he was watching you when you were looking for me, and now I have special orders about you." The lama looked at me, smiling slightly, possibly amused at the expression which I knew was on my face. More trouble, I thought, more tales of woe to come, more hardships to endure now so that they won't appear so bad in the future by comparison. I am sick of hardship, I thought to myself. Why can't I be like some of those people who flew those kites in a battle, or drove those roaring steam boxes with a lot of soldiers? I thought, too, I would rather like to be in charge of one of those metal things which floated on water and took a lot of people between countries. Then my attention wandered, and I pondered the question—how could they be metal? Anyone would know that metal was heavier than water and so would sink. There must be a catch to it, I decided; they could not be metal at all, that monk must have been telling me a story. I looked up to see my Guide laughing at me; he had been following my thoughts by telepathy, and he really was amused.

"Those kites are airplanes; the steam dragon is a train, and those iron boxes are ships, and—yes—iron ships really do float. I will tell you all about it later, but for the moment we have other things in mind." He rang his bell again, and a serving-monk entered and removed the table which had been before me, smiling ruefully at all the havoc I had made of the foods from India. My Guide said we wanted more tea, and we waited while a fresh lot was brought to us. "I prefer Indian tea to China tea," said my Guide. I agreed with him; China tea always rather sickened me; I did not know why because I was obviously more used to China tea, but the Indian tea seemed to be more pleasant. Our discussion on the matter of tea was interrupted by the serving-monk bringing in a fresh supply. He withdrew as my Guide poured fresh cups of tea.

"His Holiness has said that you be withdrawn from the ordinary standard classes. Instead, you are to move into an apartment next to mine, and you are to be taught by me and by the leading lama specialists. You have the task of preserving much of the ancient knowledge, and later you will have to put much of that knowledge into writing, for our most alert seers have forecast the future of our country saying that we shall be invaded, and much that is in this lamasery and others will be ravaged and destroyed. Through the wisdom of the Inmost One certain records are already being copied so that the copies will remain here to be destroyed and the originals will be taken far, far away where no invader will be able to reach. First, you will have to be taught extensively about the metaphysical arts." He stopped speaking and rose to his feet, and moved into another room. I heard him rustling about, and then he came back carrying a very plain wooden box which he brought and placed on the ornamental table. He sat down before me and for a moment or two remained silent.

"Years and years ago people were very different from what they are now. Years and years ago people could call upon the natural laws and use senses which humanity has now lost except in certain rare instances. Many hundreds of centuries ago people were telepathic and clairvoyant, but through using such powers for evil purposes, humans as a whole have lost the ability, the whole of those powers now are atrophied. Worse—humans now generally deny the existence of such powers. You will find when you move about to different countries that when you leave Tibet and India it will not be wise to talk of clairvoyance, astral travelling, levitation, or telepathy, because people will merely say, 'Prove it, prove it, you talk in riddles, you talk nonsense, there is no such thing as this, or that, or something else, if there were science would have discovered it.' "

He withdrew into himself for a moment, and a shadow crossed his features. He had travelled extensively, and although he looked young—well, actually he looked ageless, one could not say if he were an old man or a young man, his flesh was firm and his face fairly unlined, he radiated health and vitality—yet I knew that he had travelled to far-away Europe, travelled to Japan, China, and India. I knew, too, that he had had some most amazing experiences. Sometimes when he was sitting he would look at some magazine which had been brought over the mountains from India, and then he would sigh with sorrow at the folly of warring mankind. There was one particular magazine which really interested him, and whenever he could he had it brought from India. It was a peculiar sort of magazine called *London Illustrated*. I found odd copies of the magazine to be a great source of information, giving me pictures about things quite beyond my understanding. I was interested in what were called "advertisements," and whenever I could I tried to read the pictures and then, as opportunity presented itself, I would find someone who knew enough of the strange language to tell me about the wording.

I sat and looked at my Guide. Occasionally I looked at the wooden box which he had brought out, and wondered what it could possibly contain. It was a box of some wood quite foreign to me. It had eight sides to it so that, as near as anything, it was round. I sat for some time wondering what it was all about, what was in it, why he had suddenly lapsed into silence. Then he spoke, "Lobsang, you have to develop your very high degree of natural clairvoyance to an even higher state, and the first thing is to get to know this." Briefly he motioned to the eight-sided wooden box as if that would explain everything, but it just led me into a deeper state of confusion. "I have here a present which is given to you by order of the Inmost One himself. It is given to you to use and with it you can do much good." He leaned forward and with two hands picked up the wooden box, and looked at it for a few moments before putting it in my hands. He put it very carefully in my hands and held his own hands near by in case I—boylike—should be clumsy and drop it. It had a surprising weight, and I thought it must have a lump of stone inside it to be so heavy.

"Open it, Lobsang!" said the Lama Mingyar Dondup. "You will not get any information about it by just looking at the box."

Dumbly I turned the thing in my hands, hardly knowing how to open it because it was eight-sided and I could not see how the top fitted on. But then I grasped the top and somehow gave it a half-twist. The top domed portion came off in my hands. I peered at it and it was just a lid, so I put it down beside me while I devoted my attention to what was in the box. All I could see was a lump of cloth, so I grasped that and went to lift it out, but the weight was quite amazing. I spread my robe carefully so that if there was anything loose inside it would not fall on the floor, and then with my hands over the box I inverted the box and took the weight of the contents on my fingers. I put down the now empty box and devoted my attention to the spherical object wrapped up in dead, black cloth.

As my busy fingers unwrapped the thing, I gasped in fascinated awe, for revealed to me now was a very wonderful, quite flawless crystal. It was indeed crystal, not like the glass used by fortunetellers, but this crystal was so pure that one could hardly see where it began and ended, it was almost like a sphere of nothingness as I held it in my hands—that is, until I contemplated the weight, and the weight was quite formidable. It weighed as much as a stone of the same size would weigh.

My Guide looked at me smiling. As I met his eyes he said, "You have the right touch, Lobsang, you are holding it in the correct manner. Now you will have to wash it before you can use it, and you will have to wash your hands, too!"

"Wash it, Honorable Lama!" I said in some amazement. "Whatever should I wash it for? It is perfectly clear, perfectly clean."

"Yes, but it is necessary that any crystal be washed when it changes hands, because that crystal has been handled by me, and then the Inmost One handled it, and I handled it after. So now, you do not want to delve into my past or my future, and it is, of course, forbidden to delve into the past, present, or future of the Inmost One. Therefore, go into the other room," he motioned with his hand to the direction I should take, "and wash your hands, then wash the crystal, and make sure that you pour water over it so that it will be running water. I will wait here until you have finished."

Very carefully I wrapped up the crystal and eased myself off the cushion where I had been sitting, placing the crystal on its center so that it could not fall off onto the ground. When I had regained my feet and was standing more or less securely, I reached and lifted the cloth-wrapped bundle and left the room. It was a beautiful thing to hold in water. As I rubbed my hands around it under the water it seemed to glow with life, it felt as if it were part of me, it felt as if it belonged to me, as indeed it now did. I gently set it aside and washed my own hands, making sure that I used plenty of fine sand, and then I rinsed them and went back and rewashed the crystal, holding it beneath a jug which I held inverted while the water splashed over the crystal making a little rainbow as the falling drops were struck by the incoming sunlight. With the crystal clean, and my hands clean too, I returned to the room of my Guide, the Lama Mingyar Dondup.

"You and I are going to be much closer in the future, we are going to live next door to each other, for so the Inmost One has decreed. You are not to sleep in the dormitory after this night. Arrangements are being made whereby when we return to Chakpori tomorrow you will have a room next to mine. You will study with me, and you will study with learned lamas who have seen much, done much, and travelled in the astral. You will also keep your crystal in your room, and no one else must touch it because it would give a different influence to it. Now move your cushion and sit with your back to the light."

I shuffled around and sat with my back to the light. I sat rather close to the window carefully clutching the crystal in my hands, but my Guide was not satisfied. "No, no, be sure that no ray of light falls on the crystal, for if it does you will make false reflections within. It is necessary that there be no points of light in the crystal, instead you must be aware of it, but not aware of its exact circumference." He rose to his feet, and pulled an oil-silk curtain over the window, subduing the sunlight, and making the room flood with a pale-blue glow, almost as if twilight had come upon us.

It should be said that we had very little glass in Lhasa, or rather, very little glass in Tibet, because all glass had to be brought across the mountains on the backs of traders or on the backs of their pack-animals, and in the sudden storms which beset our city glass would be shattered immediately by the wind-driven stones. Thus, we had shutters made of odd materials, some were of wood and others were of oil-silk or similar odd materials which shut out the wind and shut out the dust, but the oil-silk was the best because it let sunlight filter through.

At last I was in a position which my Guide considered to be suitable. I was sitting with my legs tucked under me—not in the lotus position because my legs had been too much damaged for that—but I was sitting with my legs tucked under me and my feet were protruding to the right. In my lap my cupped hands held the crystal, held it beneath so that I could not see my hands under the bulging sides of that globe. My head was bowed, and I had to look at the crystal or in the crystal without actually seeing, without actually focusing. Instead, to see correctly in a crystal, one focused at a point in infinity, because if one focused directly at the crystal one focuses automatically on any smear, or speck of dust, or on any reflection, and that usually destroys the effect. So—I was taught to always focus at some point in infinity while apparently looking through the crystal.

I was reminded of my experience in the temple when I had seen the wandering souls come in range, and where the nine lamas had been doing their chant, punctuating each reference to a stick of incense by the tinkling of a silver bell.

My Guide smiled across at me, and said, "Now there is no time to do any crystal gazing or scrying for the moment because you will be taught properly, and this is a case of 'more haste less speed.' You want to learn how to hold the thing properly, as indeed you are doing now, but you want to learn the different methods of holding for different occasions. If you want world affairs you use the crystal on a stand, or if you want to read about one individual you take the crystal and let the inquirer hold it first, after which you take it from him and, if you are properly trained, you can see that which he wants to know."

Just at that moment pandemonium broke out above us; there was the deep, roaring, discordant sound of the conches like yaks lowing in the meadows, a ululating sound which wobbled up and down the scale like an excessively fat monk trying to waddle along. I could never discern any music in the conches; others could, and they told me it was because I was tone deaf! After the conches came the blare of the temple trumpets, and the ringing of bells, and the beating of wooden drums. My Guide turned to me and said, "Well, Lobsang, you and I had better go to the Service because the Inmost One will be there, and it is common courtesy for us to go on our last evening here at the Potala. I must hurry off, you come at your own speed." So saying, he rose to his feet, gave me a pat on the shoulder and hurried out.

Very carefully I wrapped up my crystal, wrapped it very, very carefully indeed, and then with the utmost caution I put it back in its eight-sided wooden box. I put it on the table by the seat of my Guide, the Lama Mingyar Dondup. And then I, too, followed down the corridor.

Acolytes, monks, and lamas were hurrying along from all directions. It reminded me of a disturbed colony of ants rushing along. People seemed to be in a hurry so that they could get in the best position relative to their own class. I was in no hurry so long as I got in somewhere and could sit without being seen, that was all I asked.

The sound of the conches ceased. The blaring of the trumpets ended. By now the stream entering the Temple had diminished to a trickle and I found myself following at the tail end. This was the Great Temple, the Temple at which attended the Inmost One himself when he had time from his world duties to come and mix with the lamas.

The great pillars supporting the roof seemed to soar up into the blackness of night. Above us there were the ever-present clouds of incense smoke, greys, and blues, and whites, swirling and intermingling and yet never seeming to settle out into one particular shade, for all these clouds of incense seemed in some way to retain their own individuality.

Small boys were rushing around with flaring torches lighting more and more butter lamps, which sputtered and hissed, and then burst into flames. Here and there, there was a lamp which had not been properly lighted because one had first to rather melt the butter so that it became liquid like oil, otherwise the wick which should be floating merely charred and smoldered, and made us sneeze with the smoke.

At last sufficient lamps were lit, and huge sticks of incense were brought out and they, too, were lit, and then extinguished so that they glowed red and gave out great clouds of smoke. As I looked about me, I saw all the lamas in one group in rows facing each other, and the next row would be back to back, and so on facing each other, and the next row would be back to back. Farther out from them were the monks sitting in a similar manner, and beyond those the acolytes. The lamas had little tables about a foot high on which reposed various small items, including the ever-present silver bell; some had wooden drums, and later as the Service started the Lector standing at his lectern would read out passages from our Sacred Books, and the lamas and monks in unison would chant, and the lamas would, at the completion of each passage, ring their bells, while others would tap with their fingers on the drums. Again and again, to signify the end of some particular part of the Service, there would be the rumbling of the conches from somewhere in the distance, somewhere in the dim recesses of the Temple. I looked on, but it was merely a spectacle to me; it was merely religious discipline, and I decided that some time when I had time I would ask my Guide why it was necessary to go through the ceremony. I wondered if it made people any better because I had seen so many monks who were very devout, very devoted indeed to their service attendances, but away from the temples, away from the services, they were sadistic bullies. Yet others who never went near the temples were kindhearted and considerate, and would always do something to help the poor bewildered small boy who didn't know what to do next and who was always afraid of getting into trouble because so many adults hated to be asked things by small boys.

I looked to the center of the Temple, the center of the lamastic group, and I looked at our revered, be-loved Inmost One sitting there, serene and calm with a very strong aura of spirituality, and I resolved that I would at all times try to model myself on him and on my Guide, the Lama Mingyar Dondup.

The Service went on and on, and I am afraid that I must have fallen asleep behind one of the pillars because I knew nothing more until there was the loud ringing of bells and the roaring of conches again, and then the sound as of a multitude rising to their feet and the indefinable noises which a lot of men make when they are making for an exit. So I rubbed my eyes with my knuckles, and tried to look intelligent, tried to look awake and as if I had been paying attention.

Wearily I went along, again at the tail end, to our common dormitory, thinking how glad I was that after this night I should not be sleeping with a whole crowd of boys who rent the night with their snores and cries, but after this night I should be able to sleep alone.

In the dormitory, as I prepared to wrap myself in my blanket, a boy was trying to talk to me, saying how wonderful he thought it was that I was going to have a place of my own. But he yawned heavily in the middle of his sentence and just fell to the ground, sound asleep. I walked to the window wrapped in my blanket, and looked out again at the starry night, at the spume of snow tearing away from the mountain tops and lit most beautifully by the rays of the rising moon. Then I, too, lay down and slept, and thought of nothing. My sleep was dreamless and peaceful.

CHAPTER ELEVEN

TOGETHER we walked down the corridors until at last we reached the inner courtyard where monk-grooms were already holding two horses, one for my Guide, the Lama Mingyar Dondup, and the other for unfortunate me! My Guide motioned to a groom to help me mount, and I was glad my legs were bad because a horse and I rarely arrived at the same point together; if I went to mount a horse, the horse moved and I fell to the ground, or if I expected the horse to move and took a running jump the horse did not move and I jumped right over the wretched creature. But this time with the excuse of my injured legs, I was helped onto that horse, and immediately I did one of those things which are NOT DONE! I started riding away without my Guide. He laughed out loud as he saw me, knowing that I had no control over that unfortunate horse. The horse strode away out of the courtyard and down the path, I clutching on for dear life, afraid of rolling over the mountain side.

Around by the outer wall I rode. A fat and friendly face peered out of a window just above and called, "Good-by, Lobsang, come again soon, we'll have some fresh barley in next week, good stuff, better stuff than we've been having lately. You call and see me as soon as you come." The cook-monk heard another horse coming and turned his eyes to the left, and let out a "Ow! Ai! Ai! Honorable Medical Lama, forgive me!" My Guide was coming and the poor cook-monk thought that he had been impertinent, but my Guide's friendly smile soon put him at ease.

I rode off down the mountain, my Guide chuckling

behind me. "We shall have to coat the horse with glue for you, Lobsang," he chortled. I looked back rather glumly at him. It was all right for him; he was a big man, some six feet tall and more than two hundred pounds in weight, he had muscles, he had brains, and I had no doubt that if he felt like it he could pick up that horse and carry it down the mountain side instead of the horse carrying him. I, on the other hand, felt like a fly perched on the creature. I had little control over the thing and every so often, out of the perverseness of its nature and knowing that I was scared stiff, it would go to the very edge of the path and stare straight down at the willow grove so far below, neighing presumably with amusement as it did so.

We reached the bottom of the mountain and went along the Dopdal Road because before going on to Chakpori we had a call to make in one of the offices of the government in the Village of Shö. Arrived there, my Guide very considerately tied my horse to a post and lifted me off saying, "Now you just stay around here, Lobsang, I shall be not more than ten minutes." He picked up a bag and strode off into one of the offices, leaving me sitting on a pile of stones.

"There! There!" said a countrified voice behind me. "I saw the Lama of the Saffron Robe get off that horse and here is his boy to look after the horses. How do you do, young Master?" I looked around and saw a small group of pilgrims. They had their tongues out in the traditional Tibetan greeting with which the inferiors greeted their superiors. My chest swelled with pride, I basked unashamedly in the glory reflected from being "the boy of the Lama of the Saffron Robe."

"Oh!" was my reply. "You should never come upon a priest unexpectedly like that; we are always engaged in meditation, you know, and a sudden shock is very bad for our health." I frowned rather disapprovingly as I looked toward them and continued, "My Master and Guide, the Lama Mingyar Dondup, the wearer of the Saffron Robe, is one of the most important lamas here, he is a very great person indeed, and I should not advise you to get too near his horse because his horse, too, is important bearing such a great rider. But get along now, get along, don't forget your circuit of the Ring Road, it will bring much good to you!" With that I turned away hoping that I had acted as a true monk should, hoping that I had made a favorable impression.

A chuckle near by me made me look up rather guiltily. A trader was standing there picking at his teeth with a piece of straw, one hand on his hip, the other hand very busy with his mouth. Hastily I looked around and saw the pilgrims had, as ordered, continued on their round. "Well? What do you want?" I said to the old trader who was peering at me through screwed-up eyes, his face seamed and wrinkled with the years. "I have no time to waste!" I said.

The old fellow smiled benignly. "Now, now, young Master, don't be so harsh on a poor old trader who has such a difficult time making a living in these hard, hard days. Do you happen to have any trinkets with you, anything that you have brought from the Big House up above there? I can offer you a very good price for cuttings from a lama's hair or for a piece of a lama's robe. I can offer you a better price for anything that has been blessed by one of the higher lamas such as your Master of the Saffron Robe. Speak up, young Master, speak up before he comes back and catches us."

I sniffed as I looked at him and thought, no, not if I had a dozen robes would I sell for things to be traded by fakes and charlatans. Just then, to my joy, I saw my Guide coming. The old trader saw him too and made off with a shambling gait.

"What are you trying to do, buy up traders?" asked my Guide. "No, Honorable Master," was my response, "he was trying to buy up you or any bits or pieces of you, hair pieces, robe clippings, or anything which he thinks I should have been able to steal from you." The Lama Mingyar Dondup laughed, but there was a rueful sort of ring to his laugh as he turned and stared after the trader who was not tarrying but really hurrying to get out of calling range. "It is a pity these fellows are always on the make. It is a pity they try to get something and give it a false value. After all, it is not the Saffron Robe that matters, but the soul of the wearer of the Saffron Robe." So saying he lifted me in one swift easy motion and put me astride my horse which looked as surprised as I felt. Then he untied the reins, giving them to me (as if I knew what to do with them!) and mounting his own horse, we rode off.

Down the Mani Lhakhand we went, past the rest of the Village of Shö, past the Pargo Kaling, and then over the little bridge which spanned a tributary of the Kaling Chu. We took the next turn left, passing the small Kundu Park, and taking the next road left to our own Chakpori.

This was a rough and stony road, a hard road to traverse, a road which needed a sure-footed horse. Iron Mountain, as was our name for Chakpori, is higher than the mountain on which the Potala is erected, and our pinnacle of rock was smaller, sharper, steeper. My Guide led the way, his horse every so often dislodging small stones which rolled down the path toward me. My horse followed, carefully picking a path. As we rode up I looked over to my right—to the south—whence flowed the Happy River, the Kyi Chu. I could also see straight down into the Jewel Park, the Norbu Linga, where the Inmost One had his very few moments of recreation. At present the park was very much deserted; except for a few monk-gardeners straightening up after the recent tempest, there were no senior lamas in sight. I thought how, before my legs were damaged, I liked to slither down the mountain side and duck across the Lingkor Road and go into the Jewel Park or Norbu Linga by what I thought was my own super-secret way.

We reached the top of the mountain, we reached the stony space before the Chakpori walls, walls which enclosed the whole of that lamasery. The monk at the gate quickly welcomed us in; two other monks hurried to take our horses from us. I parted from mine with the greatest of joy, but groaning somewhat as the weight fell upon my legs once again. "I shall have to see about your legs, Lobsang; they are not healing so well as I expected," said my Guide. A monk took the lama's luggage and hurried off with it. He turned and made his way into the lamasery, calling over his shoulder, "I will see you again in an hour's time."

The Potala was too public for me, too "grand," one always had to be alert in case one accidentally annoyed a senior monk or a junior lama; the senior lamas never took offence, they had greater things to worry about than whether a person was looking in their direction or apparently ignoring them. As in all cases, it is only the inferior men who create commotions, their superiors were kind, considerate, and understanding.

I wandered into the courtyard, thinking that this would be a good opportunity to have a meal. At that stage of my career, food was one of the most important things because tsampa, with all its virtues, still left one feeling quite hungry!

As I walked the well-known corridors I met many of my contemporaries, boys who had entered at much the same time as I had. But now there was a great change. I was not just another boy, not just another young lad to be trained or to be fought with; instead, I was under the special protection of the great Lama Mingyar Dondup, the wearer of the Saffron Robe. Already rumor had leaked out and had spread abroad that I was going to be specially taught, that I was going to have a room in the Lamas' Quarters, that I was going to do this, that I was going to do that, and I was amused to notice that my exploits, real or imagined, were already well known. One boy chortled gleefully to another that he had actually seen me picked up from the ground by a great gust of wind and blown up onto the top of the Golden Roof. "I saw it with my very own eyes," he said. "I was standing here at this very spot and I saw him down there sitting on the ground. Then this great dust storm came and I saw Lobsang sailing upward, he looked as if he were fighting devils on the roof. Then——" The boy paused dramatically and rolled his eyes for emphasis. "And then—he fell down right into the arms of one of the temple-keeper lamas." There was a sigh of awe, admiration, and envy all mixed, and the boy continued, "And then Lobsang was taken to the Inmost One which brought distinction and honor to our class!"

I pushed my way through the throng of sensation-seekers, the horde of small boys and junior monks who were hoping that I would make some startling announcement, a sort of revelation from the gods, but I was in search of food; I pushed my way through that throng and stumped off down the corridor to a well-known spot—the kitchen.

"Ah! So you've returned to us, eh? Well, sit ye down, lad, sit ye down, I'll feed you up well. You've not been too well fed at the Potala by the look of you. Sit ye down and I'll feed you." The old cook-monk came and patted my head and pushed me back so that I was sitting on a pile of empty barley sacks. Then he just fished inside my robe and managed to get my bowl. Off he went, carefully cleaning my bowl all ready (not that it needed it!), and off to the nearest of the cauldrons. Soon he was back slopping tsampa and tea all over the place, making me draw up my legs in case I got it over my robe. "There, there, boy," he said, pushing the bowl into my hands. "Eat it up, eat it up quick, because I know you will be sent for soon—the Abbot wants to hear all about what happened." Fortunately, someone else came in and wanted attention so he turned away from me and went off leaving me to eat my tsampa.

With that matter disposed of, I thanked him politely because he was a good old man who thought that boys were nuisances, but that they were not such nuisances if they were fed properly. I went to the great bin of fine sand and carefully cleaned my bowl once again, taking the broom and sweeping up the sand which I had spilled on the floor. I turned and bowed in his direction, to his pleased surprise, and made my way out.

I went to the end of the corridor and rested my arms against the wall while I peered out. Below me was the swamp, a bit beyond that was the flowing stream. But I was looking over the Kashya Linga toward the ferry because the boatman appeared to be most uncommonly busy today. He was there standing up leaning on his oars, pushing away at them working hard, and his yak-skin boat seemed to be absolutely laden down with people and their bundles, and I wondered what it was all about, why there were so many people flocking to our Holy City. Then I remembered the Russians, the Russians had been putting a lot of pressure on our country because the British had been making a commotion also, and now the Russians were sending a lot of spies into Lhasa disguised as traders and thinking that we poor ignorant natives would never know. They forgot, or perhaps never even knew, that many of the lamas were telepathic and clairvoyant and knew what they were thinking almost as soon as they themselves knew.

I loved to stand and watch and see all the different types of people, and to divine their thoughts, determine whether they were good or bad. With practice it was easy, but now was hardly the time for standing staring at others, I wanted to go and see my Guide, I wanted to be able to lie down. My legs were hurting me and I really was tired. My Guide had had to go away to the Wild Rose Fence before I was really well enough to get about my business. Actually, I should have been between my blankets on the floor for another week, but the Chakpori—good place though it was—it really did not welcome small boys who were ill, who had wounds which were slow to heal, and who broke the regular routine. So it was that I had had to go to the Potala where there were, curiously enough, more facilities for such attentions than in our "Temple of Healing."

At Chakpori suitable students were taught the healing arts. We were taught all about the body, how the different parts of the body work, we were taught acupuncture in which very thin needles are pushed into the body to stimulate certain nervous centers, and we were taught about herbs, how to gather herbs after having been able to identify them, how to prepare them, store them, and dry them. In the Chakpori we had large buildings in which monks under the supervision of lamas were always preparing ointments and herbs. I remembered the first time that I had seen them.

I peered through the doorway, hesitant, scared, not knowing what I would see, not knowing who would see me. I was curious because, although my studies had not yet reached the state of herbal medicine, I was still vastly interested. So—I peered.

The room was large, it had a high, raftered roof, and from great beams which stretched from side to side and which held up a triangular arrangement of frames, ropes descended. For a time I looked, not being able to understand the purpose of those ropes. Then as my eyes became sharper in the somewhat dim interior, I saw that the other end of the ropes were attached to leather bags, leather bags which by suitable treatment were as hard as wood. Each leather bag had a word painted on it, words which meant not a thing to me. I watched and no one took any notice of me until at last an old lama turned and saw me. He smiled quite kindly and said, "Come in, my boy, come in. I am pleased indeed to see that one so young is already taking an interest. Come in." Hesitantly I walked toward him, and he put a hand on my shoulder and to my amazement he started telling me about the place, pointing out the different herbs, telling me the difference between herb powder, herb tea, and herb ointment. I liked the old man, he seemed to have been remarkably sweetened by his herbs!

Just in front of us there was a long table of stone, a rather rough type of stone. I would not like to say what sort of stone it was, but it was probably granite. It was level and about fifteen feet by six feet, one large solid slab. Along its sides monks were very busy spreading herb lumps, that is the only word I can find to describe them because they seemed to be clotted lumps of herbs, a mass of brownish vegetation. They spread these herbs on the table, and then with flat pieces of stone something like bricks, they pressed down on the herbs, dragging the stone toward the side. As they lifted I found that the herbs were being macerated—shredded. They kept on and kept on at it until it seemed that only a fibrous pulp was left. When they reached that stage they stood back and other monks approached with leather pails and stones with a serrated edge. Carefully the fresh lot of monks scraped the stone bench, scraped all the fibrous matter into their leather pails. With that done, the original monks spread fine sand on the bench and started rubbing it with their stones, cleaning it and at the same time making fresh scratches which would hold the herbs so that they could be shredded.

The monks with their leather pails took the fibrous material to the far side of the large room where, I now saw, there were steaming cauldrons of water. One after the other they took their pails and emptied the contents into one of the cauldrons. I was interested to see that it had been bubbling and steaming, but as soon as the new fibrous stuff was put in the boiling stopped. The old lama took me across and looked in, and then he picked up a stick and stirred the stuff, saying, "Look! We are boiling this, and we are keeping on boiling it until the water boils off and we get a thick syrup. I will show you what we do with that."

He led me across to another part of the hall, and there I saw great jars full of syrup all labelled with their different identities. "This," he remarked, pointing to one particular jar, "is what we give to those suffering from catarrhal infections. They have a small amount of this to drink and, while the taste is not very pleasant, it is much more pleasant than the catarrh. Anyway, it cures them!" He chuckled in high good humor, and then led me to another table in an adjacent room. Here I found that a group of monks were working on a stone bench, it seemed to be a shallow trough. They had wooden paddles in their hands and they were mixing up a whole collection of things under the supervision of another lama. The old lama who was giving me such a pleasant conducted tour said, "Here we have oil of eucalyptus, together with oil of camphor. We mix that with some highly expensive imported olive oil, and then with these wooden paddles the monks stir everything up and mix it with butter. The butter forms a fine base for an ointment. When we have people with chest afflictions they find fine relief when this is rubbed on their chest and back." Gingerly I stretched out a finger and touched a blob of the stuff on the edge of the trough, even more cautiously I sniffed it and I even felt my eyes going crossed. The smell seemed to burn right through me, it seemed as if my lungs were going to burn inside out, and I was afraid to cough, although I badly wanted to, in case I should explode. The old lama laughed and laughed as he said, "Now put that on your nose and it will take the skin out of your nostrils. That is the concentrated stuff, it has to be diluted yet with more butter."

Farther along monks were stripping the tips off the leaves of a certain dried plant, and carefully sifting it through a cloth which was like a very close mesh net. "These monks are preparing special teas. By tea we mean an admixture of herbs which can be drunk. This particular tea," he turned and pointed, "is an anti-spasmodic tea and it gives relief in cases of nervous twitchings. When you come here and take your turn at all this you will find it extremely interesting." Just then someone called to him, but he said before leaving, "Look around, my boy, look around. I am glad indeed to see one who is so interested in our arts." With that he turned and hurried off to the other room.

I wandered about taking a sniff of this and a sniff of that. I took one particular powder and sniffed it so much that it got up my nostrils and down my throat, and made me cough and cough and cough, until another lama came and gave me a drink of tea, beastly stuff it was, too.

I recovered from that incident and walked to a far wall where there was a great barrel. I looked at it and I was amazed because it seemed to be full of a bark, a curious-looking bark, bark such as I had never seen before. I touched a piece and it was crumbly in my fingers. I put my head sideways in some astonishment because I couldn't see what use there would be for such dirty old pieces of bark, rougher and dirtier than anything I had seen in any of our parks. A lama looked at me, came over and said, "So you've not any idea what this is, eh?" "No, Honorable Medical Lama," I replied, "it seems to me to be just rubbish."

He laughed at that, he really was highly amused as he said, "That, young man, is a bark which is used for the most common ailment in the world today, a bark which gives relief and which has saved many lives. Can you guess what it is? What is the most common ailment?"

He really had me puzzled there, and I thought and thought, and just could not come up with any sensible solution, and I told him so. He smiled as he told me. "Constipation, young man, constipation. The biggest curse of the world. But this is a sacred bark which we import by traders from India. It is called sacred bark because it comes from a very, very distant country, Brazil, where they call it cascara sagrada, that is, bark sacred. We use it, again, as a tea, or in exceptional cases we boil and boil and boil until we have a distillate which we mix up with a certain collection of chalk and sugars, and then we press it into a pill form. That is for the ones who cannot take its acrid taste as a tea." He smiled quite kindly at me, obviously pleased at my interest, and it really was interesting.

The old lama whom I had first met came hurrying back, asking me how I was managing, and then he smiled as he saw that I was still handling a bit of cascara sagrada. "Chew it, my boy, chew it. It will do you a lot of good, it will cure any cough that you have because you will be afraid to cough after chewing that!" He chortled away like a small elf, because although he was a high medical lama he was still a small man in stature.

"Over here, over here," he said, "look at this, this is

142

from our own country. Slippery elm, we call it, the bark of the slippery elm. A very useful thing for people who have gastric disturbances. We mix it up, we make a paste of it, and the unfortunate sufferer takes the stuff and it relieves his pain. But you wait, my boy, you wait. When you come here a little later on I am sure that we shall discover that you have a great future ahead of you."

I thanked him and the other lama for their kindness, and then I left after the first of many visits.

But hurrying footsteps—hurrying footsteps; a boy was coming with the order for me to go to my Guide, the Lama Mingyar Dondup, who was awaiting me in his own quarters and which now would be almost mine, because I was going to have a room next door to him. So I wrapped my robe tightly about me, trying to look tidy again and hurried off as fast as I could, hurried off to see what sort of place I was going to have.

CHAPTER TWELVE

MINE WAS a pleasant room, small, but still large enough for my requirements. I was gratified indeed to notice that I had two low tables, and one of those low tables had quite a number of magazines and papers on it. On the other table there were some very nice things laid out for me—those sweet things of which I so heartily approved. As I entered a monk-attendant smiled at me and said, "The Gods of Fortune have certainly smiled upon you, Lobsang. You are right next door to the High Lama Mingyar Dondup." I knew that, he was telling me things I already knew, but then he said, "Here is a communicating door; you must remember never to enter that door without permission from your Guide, because he may be in deep meditation. Now you cannot see your Guide for a little time, so I suggest you get down to that food." With that he turned and left my room. My room! It sounded good. It was a wonderful thing to have a room of my own after having had to sleep very publicly with a lot of other boys.

I walked across to the table, bent down and carefully examined all the good things displayed there. After a frenzy of uncertainty I decided which I would have, a sort of a pink thing with a white dusting on top. I picked it up with my right hand and then for good measure I picked up another with my left hand, then I went to the window to see just where I was in the building.

I rested my arms on the stone of the recessed windowframe and poked my head outside, muttering a very unfortunate word as I dropped one of my Indian cakes in the process. Hastily I gobbled up the other lest it, too, should share that fate, then I returned to my scrutiny of the landscape.

Here, I was at the extreme South Eastern part of the building, I had the last room right on the corner of the annex. I could see the Jewel Park—The Norbu Linga. At present there were a number of lamas poking about, they seemed to be having a debate, making quite a number of gestures. For a few idle moments I watched them; they were quite amusing, one was posturing on the ground and the other was declaiming to him, then they changed places. Oh!—yes, I knew what they were doing, they were rehearsing for the public debates because the Dalai Lama himself was going to take part in a public lamastic debate. Satisfied that I had not missed anything that I should know about, I turned to other things.

A few pilgrims were pottering about on the Lingkor Road—pottering about as if they expected to find gold beneath every bush or beneath every stone. They were a motley collection, some of them were orthodox pilgrims, really sincere; others, as I could tell without much trouble, were spies, Russian spies who were spying upon the Chinese and us, and Chinese spies who were spying on the Russians and on us. I thought that as long as they spied on each other they might leave us alone! Right below my window was a swamp with a little river running through it and emptying into the Happy River. There was a bridge over the river which carried the Lingkor Road. I watched in some amusement because there was a small group of townsboys there—Black Heads, we called them, because they hadn't shaven heads as we monks had. They were fooling about on this bridge, throwing little bits of wood over one side and dashing across to the other side to see them reappear. One boy overbalanced with a suitable assist from one of his companions, and over he went, head first into the water. However, it was not very serious, he managed to drag himself ashore covered in a particularly gluey mud which already I, to my cost, had encountered in that river. Then all the boys rushed down the bank and helped him get clean because they knew what mother and father would say to each of them if they all went back into Lhasa City and left the boy in such a horrid state.

More to the East the boatman was still plying his trade, ferrying across the river, making a great production of it in the hope of being able to drag a little more money out of his passengers. This was a thing that really interested me, because at that time I had never been on the water in a boat, and at that time it was really the height of my ambition.

A little farther along the ferry road was another small park, the Kashya Linga, along the road which led to the Chinese Mission. I could actually see the Chinese Mission walls from my room, and I could look down on the garden even though it was well shielded by trees. We boys always thought that horrible atrocities were taking place in the Chinese Mission, and—who knows? It may be that we were correct!

More to the East was the Khati Linga, a very pleasant but somewhat damp park, located in swampy ground. Farther away was the Turquoise Bridge which I could see, and the sight of which delighted me. I thoroughly enjoyed seeing people enter the covered enclosure, later to emerge at the other end.

Beyond the Turquoise Bridge I could see the City of Lhasa, the Council Hall, and, of course, the golden roofs of the Jo Kang, the Cathedral of Lhasa which was perhaps the oldest building in our country. Far beyond were the mountain ranges and the dotted hermitages, and the great heaps of different lamaseries. Yes, I was well satisfied with my room, and then it occurred to me that I could not see the Potala. Simultaneously the thought occurred to me that high officials of the Potala could not see me either, so if I dropped pebbles or lumps of tsampa onto unsuspecting pilgrims no one would see me, and the pilgrims would put it down to birds!

In Tibet we did not have beds, we slept on the floor. Most times we did not have cushions or anything else on the floor, we just wrapped ourselves in blankets and lay down, perhaps using our robes as a pillow. But it was not time to retire; instead I sat with the window at my back so that the light streamed in over my shoulders, and I picked up a magazine. The title meant nothing to me because it might have been English, French, or German, I could not read any of them. But as I turned to this particular magazine it appeared to be an Indian one, because they had a sort of map on the cover and I could recognize some of the names, some of the shapes of the words.

I turned over the pages. The words meant nothing to me, and I devoted myself exclusively to the pictures. As I sat there feeling content, feeling that my lot had changed for the better, I was quite happy to just look at pictures while my thoughts wandered far afield. Idly I turned the pages, and then I stopped and laughed and laughed and laughed to myself; here in the two center pages were a collection of pictures of men standing on their heads tying themselves into knots and all sorts of things of that nature. Now I knew what I was seeing—some of the yoga exercises which were then very much the cult in India. I laughed hard and loud at some of the expressions, then stopped suddenly as I looked up and saw my Guide, the Lama Mingyar Dondup, smiling at me through the open communicating door.

Before I could scramble to my feet he waved me down, saying, "No, we want no formality here, Lobsang. Formality is suitable for formal occasions, but this room is your home just as my room"—he motioned through the open doorway—"is my home. But what was making you laugh so much?" I suppressed my rising mirth and pointed to the yoga pictures. My Guide came into the room and sat on the floor with me.

"You should not laugh at other peoples' beliefs, you know, Lobsang, because you would not like other people to laugh at your beliefs. These"—he motioned to the pictures—"are practicing yoga. I do not do yoga, nor do any of the higher lamas do it, only those who have no ability to do metaphysical things do yoga."

"Master!" I said in some excitement. "Will you tell me something about yoga, how people do it, what it is? I am very puzzled about the whole thing."

My Guide looked at his fingers for a few moments, and then answered me, saying, "Well, yes, you have to learn about these things. Let us talk about them now. I will tell you something about yoga."

I sat and listened while my Guide talked. He had been everywhere, and seen everything, and done everything, and I wanted nothing so much as to model myself upon him. I listened with more care than a small boy would normally give as he talked to me.

"I am not interested in yoga," he said, "because yoga is merely a means of disciplining the body. If a person already has discipline of the body, then yoga becomes merely a waste of time. In this, our country, no one except the very much lower classes ever practices yoga. The Indians have made very much of a cult of yoga, and I regret that exceedingly because it is leading one away from the real truths. It is conceded that before one can do various metaphysical practices one must have control of the body, must be able to control one's breathing, one's emotions, one's muscles. But"—he smiled as he looked at me—"I am opposed to yoga because it is merely trying by brute force to do that which should be achieved by spiritual means."

While he was talking I was looking at the pictures, and it did seem remarkable that people should try to tie themselves up in knots and think it was being spiritual. But my Guide continued, "Many of the lower types of Indians can do a form of trick by indulging in yoga. They are able to do hypnotism and various other tricks which they have made themselves believe is a truly spiritual thing; instead, it is a trick, and nothing more. I have never heard of anyone going to the Heavenly Fields on the basis of being able to tie his body up in knots," he said with a laugh.

"But why do people do such remarkable things?" I asked. "There are certain things, certain physical manifestations which can be achieved by yoga, and there is no doubt that if one practices yoga, it can perhaps develop a few muscles, but that does not help in developing spirituality. Many of the Indians put on exhibitions, and such men are called fakirs. They travel from village to village and town to town putting on yoga exhibitions, perhaps tying oneself up in knots, as you call it, or keeping one's arm above one's head for a long time, or doing other remarkable things. They put on a holy pose as if they were doing the most wonderful thing of all, and because they are a noisy minority who bask in publicity people have reached the conclusion that yoga is an easy way to reach the great truths. This is completely wrong; yoga merely assists one to develop or control or discipline the body, and it does not help one achieve spirituality."

He laughed and said, "You would hardly believe this, but when I was a very young man I tried yoga myself, and I found that I was spending so much time trying to do a few childish exercises that I had not sufficient time left to devote to spiritual progress. So, on the advice of a wise old man, I gave up yoga and got down to serious business." He looked at me and then stretched his arm in the direction of Lhasa, he swung it round to include the direction of the Potala, saying, "In all our country you will not find the higher types of lama doing yoga. They get down to the real thing, and"—he raised his eyebrows and stared at me as he said this—"you will always find that the yogas make a lot of public commotion saying how wonderful they are, how important they are, and how they have the keys to salvation and spirituality. Yet the true adept of metaphysics does not talk about what he really can do. Unfortunately, in yoga it is a noisy minority which tries to sway public opinion. My advice to you, Lobsang, is this; never, never bother with yoga, for it is quite useless to you. You were born with certain powers, clairvoyance, telepathy, etc., and you have absolutely no need whatever to dabble with yoga, it could even be harmful."

While he had been talking I had been turning the

pages quite without thinking, and as I looked down I peered because I saw what seemed to be a Western man wearing a contorted expression as he was trying to do an exercise. I pointed it out to my Guide, who looked at it and said, "Ah, yes, this is a victim of yoga. A Western man who tried an exercise and dislocated a bone in the process. It is very, very unwise for Westerners to try yoga because their muscles and bones are not supple enough; one should only do yoga (if one really wants to!) if one is trained from a very early age. For middle-aged people to do it—well, it is foolish and definitely harmful. It is ridiculous, though, to say that the practice of yoga causes illness. It does not. All it does is to bring into use a few muscles, and at times a person may get a dislocation or a strained muscle, but that is the person's own fault, they should not meddle with such things." He laughed as he folded the paper and said, "The only yogi I have met have been real cranks, they have thought that they were the cleverest people ever, they thought that they knew everything, and they thought that the practice of yoga was the salvation of the world. Instead, it is just an exercise such as when you boys climb a tree or walk on stilts, and when you run so that a kite may be lofted into the air. Yoga? Just a physical exercise, nothing more, nothing spiritual. Possibly it can help one by improving one's physical condition so that then one is able to forget about yoga and get on with the things that matter, the things of the spirit. After all, in a few years everyone leaves a body, and it does not matter then if the body is full of hard muscle and strong bone, the only thing that matters then is the state of the spirit."

He returned to the subject saying, "Oh, and I should warn you of this; many practitioners of yoga forget that theirs is just a physical training cult. Instead, they have taken some of our occult healing practices and said that these healing practices are an adjunct of yoga. Such is completely false, any of the healing arts can be done by a person entirely ignorant of yoga, and

often done far better. So"—he pointed at me sternly—
"don't you ever fall victim to yoga publicity, it can
actually lead you away from the Path."

He turned and walked into his room, then he turned
back to me saying, "Oh! I have some charts here
which I want you to fix on your wall. You'd better
come and get them." Then he came over to me and
lifted me up so that I should not have the struggle of
getting up myself. I walked behind him into his room
and there on a table were three rolled papers. He held
one up saying, "This is a very old Chinese picture
which many hundreds of years ago was made in
veneered wood. It is at present in the city of Peking,
but in this representation I want you to study carefully
how the organs of the body are imitated by monks
doing various tasks." He stopped and pointed to one
particular thing. "Here," he said, "monks are busy
mixing food and fluid, that is the stomach. The monks
are preparing all this food to pass through various
pipes before it reaches other monks. If you study this
you will get a very good idea of the basic workings of
the human body."

He rolled up the scroll again, carefully tied it with
the little tapes which were already affixed to it, then he
took another and held it up for me to see. "Here," he
continued, "is a representation of the spine with various chakrams. You will see from this how the different
centers of power are located between the base of the
spine and the top of the head. This chart must be right
in front of you, so that you see it last thing at night and
first thing in the morning."

Carefully he rolled up the scroll and tied that, then
he went on to the next one, the third. He untied the
fastening and held the chart at arm's length. "Here is a
representation of the nervous system showing you
things which you will have to study, such as the cer-
vical ganglion, the vagus nerve, the cardiac plexus,
solar plexus, and pelvic plexus. All these things you
have to know because they are quite essential to you
as a medical lama in training."

I looked at the things feeling more and more despondent, because it seemed to me that I should never master all these things, all the bits and squiggles of the human body, all the wriggly bits that were nerves, and the great blobs that were chakrams. But, I thought, I've got plenty of time, let me just go at my own speed and if I cannot learn as much as they think I should—well, one cannot do more than one's best.

"Now I suggest you go out and get some air. Just put these in your room, and then whatever you do for the rest of the day is your own affair . . . unless you get into mischief!" he said with a smile. I bowed respectfully to him and picked up the three scrolls. Then I returned to my own room, shutting the communicating door between us. For a time I stood in the center of the room wondering how I should fix these wretched things, and then I observed that there were already suitable projections in the wall. Carefully I took a table and placed it beneath one of the projections; climbing the table, which gave me another foot or eighteen inches of height, I managed at last to get the cord of the first chart over the projection. Carefully I retreated to the far side of the room and looked approvingly at my handiwork. No, it was not straight. I eyed the thing critically and hurried forward to make sure that everything was correct as it should be. Satisfied that one was hanging true and level, I went to work on the other two. At last I was satisfied, and I dusted my hands together with an air of complacency. Smiling with self-satisfaction I walked out of my room wondering which way to go, but as I went out passing my Guide's door, I saw the serving-monk at the end of the corridor. He greeted me in a friendly fashion, and said, "That's the quickest way out. It is a private door for lamas, but I have been told that you are permitted to use it." He motioned to it, and I thanked him and soon slipped out into the fresh air.

I stood outside in the open. The end of the mountain path lay just beneath my feet. Over to the right a crowd of monks were busy working. It looked to me as if they were cleaning up the road, but I did not hang about, I did not want to be sent on any tasks. Instead, I moved directly forward and sat on a boulder for a time while I looked out over the city not so far away, near enough for me to distinguish in the clear, clear air of Tibet the dress of the traders, the monks, and the lamas who were going about their business.

Soon I moved a few yards down and sat on another rock beside which there was a pleasant small bush. My attention now wandered to the swamp below me, the swamp where the grass was lush and green, and where I could distinguish bubbles as fish lurked in the deeper pools. As I sat there was a sudden rushing behind me and a hoarse throaty voice said, "Hhrrah? Mmrraw!" With that there was a hearty boink in the small of my back as a solid furry head greeted me. I reached round and stroked the old cat, and he licked me, licked me with a tongue which was as rough as the gravel on the ground. Then he rushed round to the front, jumped onto my lap, jumped off, and made off through some bushes stopping just in sight, wheeling around to face me. He looked the very picture of inquiry as he stood there, tail straight up, ears straight up, facing toward me with his blue eyes glinting. I made no move, so he rushed up the hill again toward me saying, "Mrraw! Mrraw!" As I still made no move he reached out with one of his paws and hooked his claws into the bottom of my robe and gently tugged. "Oh, cat, whatever is the matter with you?" I asked in exasperation. Slowly I scrambled to my feet and looked about me to see what the cat was agitated about. There was nothing to be seen, but the cat was rushing toward a bush in the distance and then rushing back to me and clawing at my robe. So I faced down the mountain side and began a slow, cautious descent, the cat was fairly dancing with excitement, whirling around, springing into the air, and charging at me.

I clung to the bushes as I made my slow way, and I reached the point where the cat had turned to face me, but there was nothing to be seen. "Cat, you are an idiot!" I said in irritation. "You have dragged me down here just to play."

"Mmraw! Mmraw!" said the cat, clawing at my robe again and weaving about between my legs, poking beneath my robe and nibbling at my bare toes showing through my sandals.

With a sigh of resignation I progressed a bit farther, pushed my way through a bush, and clung on grimly because here was a ledge and had I not been clinging on so grimly I could have fallen over the edge. I turned to say some very unkind things to friend cat who was now in a frenzy of excitement. Darting around me he sprang over the edge. My heart nearly stopped with the shock, for the old cat was a very good friend of mine and I thought he had COMMITTED SUICIDE!

Very cautiously I sank to my knees and clinging to the bushes peered over the edge. About twelve feet below I saw the body of an aged monk. My horrified eyes saw that his head was blood-stained, and that his robe also had blood on it. His right leg, I perceived, was bent at an unnatural angle. My heart was palpitating with fright, excitement, and effort. I looked about me, and I found that just off to the left there was a small declivity down which I descended, finding myself then at the head of the old monk.

Gingerly, nearly ready to jump out of my skin with fright, I touched him. He was alive. As I touched him his eyes flickered feebly and he groaned. I saw that he had fallen over and struck his head on a rock. The cat was now sitting, watching me carefully.

Gently I stroked the old monk's head, stroking beneath the ears down the neck toward the heart. After some time his eyes opened and he looked vacantly about him. Slowly his eyes came into focus, focusing on me. "It is all right," I said soothingly. "I will go up and get help for you. I shall not be very long." The poor old man tried to smile, and closed his eyes again. I turned, and on hands and knees, as being the safest and the speediest, I made my way up to the top and rushed across the path into the concealed door of the lamas. As I entered I nearly collided with the serving-monk who was there. "Quick! Quick!" I said.

"There is a monk injured on the rocks." As I was speaking my Guide came out of his room and looked inquiringly at the commotion.

"Master! Master!" I said. "I have just found, with the aid of Honorable Puss Puss, an old monk who is injured. He has a head injury and his leg is unnaturally bent. He needs help urgently." My Guide speedily gave instructions to the serving-monk and then turned to me. "Lead on, Lobsang, I will follow," said he.

Together we went out of Chakpori and crossed the small path. I led him down the steep path, noting with consternation that his Saffron Robe was getting soiled; my own was so soiled that a few more marks made no difference! Honorable Puss Puss was there dancing about on the path ahead of us, and he really looked relieved to see the Lama Mingyar Dondup with me.

Soon we reached the old monk who still had his eyes shut. My Guide knelt down beside him and took various packages from the inner part of his robe, bandages and some stuff which he held on a piece of cloth and held beneath the old monk's nose. The monk sneezed violently and opened his eyes, eyes which were strained and painracked. He looked a very relieved monk indeed when he saw who was attending to him. "It is all right, friend, help is coming for you," said my Guide. With that the old monk closed his eyes again and sighed with relief.

My Guide raised the monk's robe and we saw bits of bone sticking through the skin of the leg just beneath the knee. My Guide said, "Hold his hands, Lobsang, hold him tightly. Rest your weight so that he cannot move. I am going to pull the leg straight." With that he caught hold of the monk's ankle, and with a very swift pull, straightened the limb and I saw the bones disappear inside the skin. It was so sudden, so carefully done, that the old man did not even have time to groan.

Quickly my Guide reached out to two branches which were very conveniently at hand on a fairly big bush. With a knife he cut them off, and padding them with a piece of his own robe, he bound them as a splint on the monk's leg. Then we just sat back to wait.

Soon there came shufflings and scufflings as a party of monks led by a lama appeared coming down the path. We called to them and directed them to the place where we were. Carefully they grouped about the old monk. One young monk, not at all carefully, tried to show off, tried to show how sure-footed he was. His foot slipped on the loose stones, his feet slipped from under him and he started to slide down the mountain side. A shrub caught the bottom of his robe and pulled it up above his head, and there he was, like a peeled banana, swinging naked to the gaze of pilgrims on the Ring Road below. My Guide chuckled, and gave orders for two others to rescue him without delay. When he was pulled back he was looking very shamefaced and very red-faced, too. I noticed that he would have to stand for a few days if he wanted to be comfortable because that place in contact with the floor when sitting was quite badly scratched by the stones!

Cautiously the monks turned the injured man so that they could slide beneath him a length of strong canvas. Then they turned him back and pulled so that he was on a convenient stretcher. They tucked the cloth right around him, forming a tube of it, and then they slid a stout pole inside, binding him to the pole by broad lengths of webbing. He was unconscious, fortunately, and then two monks raised the ends of the pole and with others behind helping by pushing and steadying their footsteps they made their slow, cautious way through the bushes, up the mountain path and into the safety of Chakpori.

I stood patting Honorable Puss Puss, telling my Guide, the Lama Mingyar Dondup, how Honorable Puss Puss had fetched me down to come to the aid of the old man. "The poor old fellow would probably have died if you had not called, Honorable Puss Puss," said my Guide, ruffling the old cat's fur. Then he turned to me saying, "Good work, Lobsang, you have started well. Keep it up."

Together we scrambled up the mountain path, both

of us envying Honorable Puss Puss who danced and gambolled ahead. My Guide entered Chakpori, but I stayed sitting on the boulder at the top, teasing Honorable Puss Puss with a piece of bark, a nice flexible piece of bark which he pretended was some fierce enemy. He leaped, and growled, and roared, and attacked the bark, and together we had the strongest sense of warm friendship.

CHAPTER THIRTEEN

IT WAS good to be back at Chakpori, good to be among those with whom I was familiar. Here the Teachers were a dedicated lot, dedicated to training medical lamas. My Guide had suggested that I should attend classes on herbs, anatomy, and medicine as Chakpori was THE center for such teaching.

With twenty-five others—boys like me, older boys, and one or two young monks from other lamaseries—I sat on the floor of one of our lecture halls; the lama Teacher was interested in his work, interested in teaching us. "Water!" he said. "Water is the key to good health. People do not drink enough to make the body function correctly. One eats—and there is a stodgy mess inside one that cannot traverse the lengthy path through the intestines. The result is a clogged system, bad digestion, and utter inability to undertake the study and practice of metaphysics." He stopped and looked about him as if to challenge us to think otherwise!

"Master," said a young monk from some lesser lamasery, "surely if we drink when we eat, we dilute our gastric juices—or so I have been told." The young monk shut up abruptly and glanced about him as if confused by his audacity.

"A good question!" said the lama Teacher. "Many people have that impression, but it is WRONG! The body has the ability to put out a highly concentrated digestive juice. So concentrated, in fact, that under certain conditions the digestive juices can start to digest the body!" We gasped in amazement, and I felt considerable fright at the thought that I was eating myself. The Teacher smiled as he saw the commotion he had caused. For a few moments more he kept silent that the full impact should dawn upon us. "Gastric ulcers, stomach irritations—how are they caused?" he asked, gazing from one to another of us in the hope of getting a reply.

"Master!" was my brash response. "When a man worries he gets ulcers in much the same way as he might get headache!"

The Teacher smiled at me and replied, "Good attempt! Yes, a man worries, the gastric juices in his stomach become more and more concentrated, until at last the weakest part of the stomach is attacked and as the acids which normally digest food erode away the weakest part and eventually make a hole, twinges of pain churn the stomach contents and lead to further concentration of the juices. At last the acids seep through the hole they have made and permeate between the layers of the stomach causing what we know as gastric ulcers. An adequate supply of water would greatly alleviate the position and could even PREVENT ulcers. Moral—when you are worried, drink water and reduce the risk of getting ulcers!"

"Master!" said a foolish boy. "I hope people do not heed this too much; I am one of those who have to carry water up the mountain side—and the work is hard enough now." Most people give no thought to the problems of a country such as Tibet. We had plenty of water, most of it in the wrong place! To supply the needs of lamaseries such as the Potala and Chakpori, teams of worker-monks and boys carried leather containers of water up the mountain paths. Laden horses and yaks also were used to transport the water necessary for our being. Endless teams of workers toiled to keep filled tanks which were placed in accessible positions. We did not just turn on a tap and find a plentiful supply—hot and cold—ours had to be dipped out of a tank. Very fine river-bed sand, also hauled up, was used for cleaning utensils and for scouring floors. Water was PRECIOUS! Our laundry was the river's edge;

we took our clothes to the river instead of carrying the river up the mountain.

The lama Teacher ignored the idiotic remark, and continued, "The worst ailment of mankind is"—he paused for dramatic effect, while we thought of plagues and cancers—"CONSTIPATION! Constipation causes more general ill-health than any other complaint. It lays the foundation for far more serious illnesses. Makes one sluggish, bad-tempered, and miserably ill. Constipation can be CURED!" Once again he paused and looked about him. "Not by massive doses of cascara sagrada, not by gallons of castor oil, but by drinking enough water. Consider—we eat. We take in food and that has to progress through our stomach and through our intestines. In the latter, short hairs called 'villi' (they are like hollow tubes) suck up nutriment from the digesting and digested food. If the food is too stodgy, too 'solid,' it cannot enter the villi. It becomes impacted into hard lumps. The intestines should 'wriggle' as we may describe the action of peristalsis; this pushes the food along the alimentary canal, making room for more. But if the food is SOLID, peristalsis merely results in pain and no movement. So—water is very necessary to soften the mass."

It is a sad fact that all medical students imagine that they have all the symptoms which they are studying. I pressed my abdomen—yes!—I was SURE that I was just one hard mass. I must do something about it, I thought. "Master!" I inquired. "How does an aperient work?" The lama Teacher's gaze turned on me. There was a smile in his eyes. I guessed that he had been watching most of us feel if we had "hard masses."

"A person who has to have an aperient is a person already deficient in body water. He is constipated because he has insufficient fluid to soften impacted waste products. Water MUST be obtained, so an aperient first causes the body to pour water THROUGH the villi so that the mass is softened and rendered pliable, then the peristaltic urge is strengthened. Pain is caused as caked lumps adhere to the inner surfaces—and the body is left dehydrated. One should ALWAYS drink much water after taking an aperient." He smiled as he added, "Of course, for our water-carrying friend, let me say that the sufferers should lie by the bank of the river and drink deeply!"

"Master! Why do constipation sufferers have such bad skin and all those pimples?" A boy with a VERY bad skin asked it, and he blushed furiously as every head swivelled in his direction.

"We should get rid of our waste products in the way intended by nature," responded our Teacher. "But if Man obstructs that method, then waste gets into the blood, clogging up the vital vessels, and the body tries to get rid of the waste through the pores of the skin. Again, the matter is not sufficiently fluid to pass through the fine tubes of the pores, and clogging and 'dirty skin' results. Drink a lot of water, do a reasonable amount of exercise—and we shall not have to pay so much for cascara sagrada, fig syrup, and castor oil." He laughed and said, "Now we will end this so that we can all rush out and lap up gallons of water!" He waved his hand in a gesture of dismissal and was walking to the door when a messenger burst in.

"Honorable Master, is there a boy Rampa— Tuesday Lobsang Rampa—here, please?"

The Teacher looked around and crooked a finger to beckon me. "You—Lobsang—what have you done this time?" he inquired mildly. I reluctantly came forward, putting on my best and most pathetic limp, and wondering what more trouble there was.

The messenger spoke to the lama, "This boy has to go to the Lord Abbot at once. I have to take him—I do not know why."

Ow! I thought, what can it be NOW? Could someone have seen me dropping tsampa on the monks? Had someone seen me put the salt in the Master of the Acolytes' tea? Or perhaps—gloomily my mind wandered over the various "sins" which I knew to be mine. What if the Lord Abbot knew SEVERAL of my offences? The messenger led the way along the cold, bare corridors of Chakpori. No luxury here, no ornate drapes as at the Potala. This was functional. At a door guarded by two Proctors the messenger stopped and muttered "Wait!" before entering. I stood and fidgeted, shifting from foot to foot, the Proctors gazed stonily at me as if I were some lesser form of human life. The messenger reappeared. "Go in!" he commanded, giving me a push.

Reluctantly I entered the door, which was pulled shut behind me. Entered—and involuntarily stopped in amazement. There was no austerity HERE! The Lord Abbot, clad in the richest vestments of red and gold, sat upon a platform raised about three feet above the floor. Four lamas stood in attendance upon him. Recovering from my shock, I bowed in the prescribed manner so fervently that my joints creaked and my bowl and charm box rattled in unison. Behind the Lord Abbot, a lama beckoned me forward, raising his hand when I reached the point at which I should stop.

Silently the Lord Abbot gazed at me, looking the whole length of me, observed my robe, my sandals, and presumably noting that I had my head well shaved. He turned to one of the Attending Lamas, "Arrumph! This is the boy, eh?"

"Yes, my Lord," replied the lama to whom he had addressed the question.

Again that stare, that calculating appraisal. "Arrumph. Urrahh! My boy, so you are he who brought aid to the Monk Tengli? Uurrmph!" The lama who had signalled me before moved his lips and pointed to me.

I got the idea; "I was so fortunate, my Lord Abbot," I replied with what I hoped was sufficient humility.

Again that gaze, inspecting me as if I were some kind of bug on a leaf. At last he spoke again, "Err, ahhh! Yes, Oh! You are to be commended my boy. Arrumphh!!" He turned his gaze elsewhere, and the lama behind him signalled for me to bow and leave. So—three more bows, and a cautious retreat backward, with a telepathic "thank you" to the lama who had guided me by such clear signals. The door bumped

162

my posterior. Gladly I fumbled behind me for the door fastening. I eased through and subsided against a wall with a "PHEW!!" of hearty relief. My eyes moved upward to meet those of a giant Proctor. "Well? Are you going to the Heavenly Fields? Don't SLUMP THERE, boy!" he bellowed in my ear. Glumly I hitched up my robe and moved down the corridor with the two Proctors looking balefully at me. Somewhere a door creaked and a voice said, "STOP!"

"My goodness, by Buddha's Tooth, what have I done now?" I asked myself in despair as I halted and turned to see what it was all about. A lama was coming toward me and—good gracious—he was SMILING! Then I recognized him as the lama who had given me signals from behind the Lord Abbot's back. "You put on a good show, Lobsang," he murmured in a pleased whisper. "You did everything just as one should. Here is a present for you—the Lord Abbot likes them, too!" He thrust a pleasantly bulky package into my hands, patted me on the shoulder, and moved off. I stood as one stupefied, fingering the packet and guessing the contents. I looked up—and the two Proctors were smiling benevolently at me—they had heard the lama's words. Ow! I said as I looked at them. A Proctor smiling was so unusual that it frightened me. Without more ado, I scurried as fast as I could out of that corridor.

"What ye got, Lobsang?" piped a small voice. I looked around and there was a boy who had recently been accepted. He was smaller than I, and he was having difficulty in settling down.

"Eats—I think!" I replied.

"Aw, gie us a taste, I missed me food," he said wistfully. I looked at him and he DID appear to be hungry. There was a storeroom off to the side; I led him in and we sat at the far wall, behind some sacks of barley. Carefully I opened the parcel and exposed the "Indian food." "Oh!" said the small boy. "I have never had food like that!" I passed him one of the pink cakes, the one with the white stuff over it. He bit and his eyes went rounder and rounder. Suddenly it dawned on me that I had been holding another cake in my left hand—but it was GONE! A sound behind me made me turn around; there was one of the cats . . . eating MY cake! And enjoying it! With a sigh of resignation I dipped into the packet again to get another cake for myself.

"Rarrh?" said a voice behind me. A paw touched my arm. "Rarrh? Mrraw!" said the voice again, and when I turned to look—he had taken my second cake and was eating it. "Oh! You HORRID thief!" I exclaimed crossly, then I remembered how good these cats were—how they were friends of mine and how they comforted me. "I am sorry, Honorable Guardian Cat," I said contritely. "You work for your living and I do not." I put my cake down and put my arms around the cat who purred and purred and purred.

"Oh!" said the small boy. "They won't let ME even TOUCH them. How do you do it?" He stretched forth his hand and "accidentally" picked up another sugar cake. As I made no comment, he relaxed and sat back that he might eat in comfort. The cat purred on and butted me with his head. I held half a cake for him, but he had had enough; he just purred even louder and rubbed the side of his face against it, spreading the gluey syrup all over his whiskers. Satisfied that I understood his thanks, he strolled away, jumped to the window sill, and sat there washing in the warm sunlight. As I turned back from watching him, I observed the small boy pick up the cake which the cat had rubbed against, and cram it into his mouth.

"Do you believe in religion?" asked the small boy. Do I believe in religion, I thought. What a truly remarkable question. Here we were training to be Medical Lamas and Buddhist Priests, and I am asked, "Do you believe in religion?" Crazy, I thought, CRAZY. Then I thought of it some more. DID I believe in religion? What DID I believe? "I didn't want to come here," said the small boy. "But they made me. I prayed to the Holy Mother Dolma; I prayed hard about not coming, and still I came. I prayed that my mother would not die, but she did die, and the Disposers of the Dead came and took her body and gave it to the vultures. I've never had a prayer answered, have YOU, Lobsang?" We sat there in the storeroom, leaning against the bags of barley. In the window the cat washed and washed and washed. Lick the forepaw, wipe it across the side of the face, lick the forepaw again, go over the top of the head behind the ears and down again to the side of the face. It was almost hypnotic as he sat and licked and cleaned, licked and cleaned, licked and cleaned. . . .

Prayer? Well now that I thought about it, prayer did not seem to work for me either! Then, if prayer did not work why did we have to pray? "I burned many sticks of incense," said the small boy, humbly. "Took them from Honorable Grandmother's special box, too, but prayers never worked for me. Look at me now— here at Chakpori training to be something that I don't want to be. WHY? WHY do I have to be a monk when I have no interest in such things?" I pursed up my lips, raised my eyebrows, and frowned just as the Lord Abbot had recently done to me.

Then I critically surveyed the small boy from head to foot. At last I said, "Tell you what, we will let the matter drop for the moment. I will think about it and let you know the answer in due course. My Guide, the Lama Mingyar Dondup, knows everything, and I will ask him to take this matter under advisement." As I turned to scramble up I saw the packet of Indian foods, now about half consumed. On an impulse I gathered the wrapping into a bundle, with, of course, the food inside, and pushed it into the astounded small boy's arms. "Here!" I said. "You have these, it will help you to think of other things than matters spiritual. Now you must go because I have to think!" I took him by the elbow and led him to the door and pushed him out. He was delighted to go, fearing that I should change my mind and want those Indian foods returned.

With him out of the way, I turned to more important matters. On one of the sacks I had seen a beautiful piece of string. I went over to it and carefully teased it out of the neck of the sack. Then I went to the window, and the cat and I had a fine game, he chasing the end of the string, leaping over sacks, diving between them, and generally having much fun. At last he and I were tired almost simultaneously. He came out, butted me, and stood with his back legs tall and his tail straight in the air, saying, "Mrrawh!" He jumped up into the window sill and disappeared on one of his mysterious journeys. I tucked the piece of cord in the front of my robe and sauntered off out through the door, along the corridor, until at last I reached my own room.

For some time I stood facing the most important picture. It was of a male figure, and one could see inside. First there was the windpipe; on the left of the windpipe a picture of two monks who were busy fanning air into the lungs. On the right two monks fanned air into the right side of the lungs, they were working quite hard, too, I observed. Then there was a picture of the heart. Here monks were busy pumping blood, or rather, fluid because one could not see that it was blood. Further on was a large chamber which was the stomach. One monk, obviously a senior monk, sat behind a table, and there were five monks very busy bringing in bundles of food. The head monk was making a tally of the amount of food being brought in.

Farther along, a group of monks were ladling bile from the gall bladder to dilute the food and to help in the matter of digestion. Yet other monks were busy in what was obviously a chemical factory—the liver— they were breaking down various substances with vats of acid, and I was quite fascinated looking at this picture, because then everything went along to coils and coils and coils which were meant to represent the intestines. Monks were stuffing various substances into the intestines. Farther on, there were the kidneys where monks were separating different fluids and seeing that they were sent off in the right direction. But below the bladder was the most interesting sight of all; two monks were sitting on opposite sides of a pipe, and they were obviously controlling the flow of fluid.

Then my gaze went back to the face of the figure, and I thought no wonder he looks so mournful with all those people inside him, and poking away at him and doing the most remarkable things to him! I stood there for some time in pleasant contemplation and fantasies concerning the little men inside.

At last there was a light tap on the communicating door and after a few moments it was opened, and I turned to see my Guide, the Lama Mingyar Dondup, standing there. He smiled with approval as he saw me studying the figure. "That is a very old figure indeed; it was made in its original form by great craftsmen of China. The original figure is exactly life-sized, and it was made out of veneers of different kinds of wood. I have seen the original and it is truly lifelike.

"I understand that you made a good impression on the Lord Abbot, Lobsang. He told me just after that he thought you had remarkable potentialities." He added in a rather ironic voice, "I was able to assure him that the Inmost One was of the same opinion!"

My head was buzzing thinking about religion, so I said humbly, "Master, can I ask you a question on a matter that has troubled me greatly?"

"Most certainly you may. If I can help you, then I will help you. What troubles you? But come, let us move into my room where we can sit comfortably and where we can have tea." He turned and led the way into his room, after a quick glance noticing that my small supply of food was becoming rapidly smaller. In his room he quickly sent for an attendant and tea was placed before us. After we had finished our meal the lama smiled at me and said, "Well, what is the trouble now? Take your time, and tell me all about it for you need not attend evening service." He sat back in the lotus position with his hands folded on his lap. I sat, or rather reclined, on my side, and tried to sort out my thoughts so that I could make the matter as clear as possible without "bumbling."

"Honorable Master," I said at last. "I am troubled on the matter of religion; I cannot see the use of religion. I have prayed and others have prayed, and nothing has come of our prayers. We seem to have been praying to a wilderness. It seems that the Gods do not listen to prayers. It seems that as this is the World of Illusion, religion and prayer must be an illusion also. I also know that many pilgrims seek the aid of lamas that their problems may be resolved, but I have never heard of any being resolved. My father, too—when I had a father!—employed a priest full time, but it does not seem to have been much good in our case. Master, can you, will you, tell me of any use in religion?"

My Guide remained silent for a time, looking at his clasped hands. At last he heaved a sigh and looked straight at me. "Lobsang," he said, "religion is a very necessary thing indeed. It is absolutely necessary, absolutely essential that there be religion which can impose spiritual discipline on its adherents. Without religion people would be worse than wild animals. Without religion there would be no voice of conscience. I say to you that it does not matter at all whether one be Hindu, Buddhist, Christian, or Jew; all men bleed red, and the faith to which they subscribe is in its essentials the same." He stopped and looked at me, trying to determine if I could follow what he was talking about, what he was meaning. I nodded, and he continued: "Here on Earth most people are very much like children in a school, children who never see the Head Teacher, who never see the world outside the school. Imagine that the school building is completely enclosed by a high wall; there are certain teachers in the school, but the head ones are never seen by this particular class. The pupils at the school would then have some grounds for thinking that there was no Head Teacher if they had not the wits to see that there was something higher than the average teacher. As the children pass their examinations and are able to go to a higher grade, then they can move outside of the wall around the school, and perhaps eventually meet the Head Teacher and see the world beyond. Too often people demand proof, they must have proof of everything, they must have proof of God, and the only way they get proof is to be able to do astral travelling, to be able to do clairvoyance, because when one can travel beyond the confines of this classroom which is walled in one can see the Greater Truth beyond." Again he stopped and looked at me rather anxiously to see if I was following his remarks satisfactorily. Actually I was and I could see complete sense in what he was saying.

"Let us imagine that we have a classroom and we believe our Head Master is called so-and-so. But there is another classroom near us and we can meet those students, they argue with us and say that the Head Master's name is something else. But a third class, whom we also can meet, breaks in rather rudely and tells us that we are all idiots because there is no Head Master because if there were we should have met him or seen him, if there were there would not be any doubt about his name. Now, Lobsang," smiled my Guide, "you will see that one classroom can be full of Hindus, they call their Head Master by one name; the next classroom can be full of Christians, they call their Head Master by another name. But when we come down to it, when we extract the essence of every religion, we find that a God is there, a Supreme Being is there. We may worship Him in many different ways, but so long as we worship Him with belief that is all that matters."

The door opened and a serving-monk brought in some fresh tea. My Guide gratefully poured some and drank, because he was thirsty with so much talking, and—well—I told myself that I had to have a drink as well because I was thirsty with listening. One excuse was as good as another!

"Lobsang, suppose all the acolytes, monks, and lamas at the Wild Rose Fence Lamasery had no one responsible for their discipline; there are seven thousand inhabitants of that lamasery, seven thousand of them. Suppose there was no discipline, suppose there was no reward, no punishment, suppose every man there could do just as he wished without anything to bother his conscience. Soon there would be anarchy, there would be murders, anything could happen. These men are kept in order by discipline, spiritual discipline as well as physical, but it is quite essential for all the peoples of the world to have a religion, for one must have spiritual discipline as well as physical discipline, because if there be physical discipline only, then it is a rule of force in which the strongest wins, but if there is a spiritual discipline one has more of a rule of love. The world today greatly needs a return to religion, not one particular religion but any religion, the religion most suited to the temperament of the person concerned."

I sat there, and I wondered about it all. I could see the sense of a discipline, but I wondered why we never got prayers answered. "Honorable Master," I asked, "that is all very well, but if religion is such a good thing for us, why is it that we do not get our prayers answered? I prayed that I would not have to come to this dump—er—I mean, lamasery, but in spite of all my prayers I had to come here. If religion is any good why should I be sent here, why were not my prayers answered?"

"Lobsang, how do you know that your prayers were not answered? You have the wrong idea about prayer. Many people think that they just clasp their hands together and ask a mysterious God to grant them an advantage over their fellows. People pray for money. Sometimes people pray that an enemy be delivered into their hands. In war opposing sides pray for victory, opposing sides say that God is on their side and is ready to smite the enemy. You must remember that when one prays, one really prays to oneself. God is not a great figure which sits at some table listening to petitions in the form of prayers and handing out whatever it is that one asks for." He laughed as he continued. "Think of going to the Lord Abbot and telling him that you were praying that he would release you from the lamasery, or he would give you a great sum of money. Do you think he would answer your request in the way you wanted him to? He would more likely answer your request in the way you didn't want him to!" It made sense to me, but it did not seem much sense to keep on praying if there was no one there to answer or to grant things which one asked, and I said so.

"But your idea of prayer, then, is an entirely selfish one. All you want all the time is something for yourself. Do you think you can pray to a God and ask him to send you a case of pickled walnuts? Do you think you can pray and have a great packet of Indian sweetmeats delivered to your arms? Prayer should be for the good of others. Prayer should be giving thanks unto God. Prayer should consist of a statement of what you want to do for others, not for yourself. When you pray you give some power to your thoughts, and if possible or convenient you should pray aloud because that adds power to the thoughts. But you should make sure that your prayers do not contradict natural laws." I was nodding a bit with all that because it did seem that prayers were not much good.

My Guide smiled at my apparent lack of attention, and he continued, "Yes, I know what you think, I know you think prayer is just a waste of time. But suppose a person had just died, or suppose a person had been dead for a few days, and you could have a prayer answered. Suppose you prayed that that person could be returned to life. Do you think it would be good to have returned to life a person who had been dead for some time? People pray that God shall strike down someone who at the moment has displeased the person praying. Do you think it would be reasonable to expect that a God would go about just killing people because some wild and woolly person had prayed to that effect?"

"But, Honorable Master, the lamas all pray in unison in the temples, and they ask various things. Then what is the purpose of that?"

"The lamas pray in unison in the temples with special things in mind. They pray—they direct their thoughts, in other words—that they may assist those in distress. They pray that those who are weary may come for assistance, telepathic assistance. They pray

171

that those who are wandering ghosts lost in the wilderness beyond this life come that they may be guided, for if a person dies knowing nothing of the other side of death, he or she may be lost in a morass of ignorance. Thus, it is that lamas pray—send out telepathic thoughts—that those who need help may come and be helped." He looked at me sternly, and added, "Lamas do not pray for their own advancement, they do not pray that they will be promoted. They do not pray that Lama so-and-so, who has been a bit difficult, shall fall off a roof or something. They pray only to help others."

My ideas were getting a bit disjointed, because I had always had the thought that a God, or the Blessed Mother Dolma, would be able to answer a prayer if it was said with sufficient fervor. For example, I had not wanted to enter a lamasery and I had prayed and prayed until my voice had almost given out. But no matter how much I had prayed, I still had had to go to the lamasery. It seemed that praying was merely something which could possibly help other people.

"I perceive your thoughts exactly, and I do not altogether agree with your views on the matter," remarked my Guide. "If one is to be spiritual one must do for others that which he would have done to him. You must pray that you may have the strength and the wisdom to bring help or strength and wisdom to others. You should not pray for your own self-gain for that is a waste and a useless exercise."

"Then," I asked, "a religion is merely something which we've got to do for others?"

"Not at all, Lobsang. A religion is something which we LIVE. It is a standard of conduct which we willingly impose on ourselves so that our Overselves may be purified and strengthened. By keeping pure thoughts, we keep out impure thoughts, we strengthen that to which we return when we leave the body. But when you are more proficient in astral travelling you will be able to see the truth for yourself. For the present—for a few more weeks—you must accept my word. Religion is very real, religion is very necessary. If you pray and your prayer is not answered as you think, it may be that your prayer was answered after all, because before we come to this Earth, we make a definite plan of what advantages and disadvantages we are going to have on this Earth. We plan our life on Earth (before we come here) just as a student in a great college plans his courses of studies so that at the end of those studies he may be this, that, or something else—that for which he trained."

"Do you think that any one religion is superior to another, Honorable Master?" I said rather timidly.

"No religion is better than the man who professes that religion. Here we have our Buddhist monks; some Buddhist monks are very good-living men, others are not so good. A religion is personal to each person; each person has a different approach to a religion, each person sees different things in his religion. It does not matter if a man is a Buddhist, a Hindu, a Jew, or a Christian. All that matters is that a person should practice his religion to the best of his belief and to the best of his ability."

"Master," I asked again, "is it right for a person to change his religion, is it right for a Buddhist to become a Christian, or a Christian to become a Buddhist?"

"My own personal opinion, Lobsang, is that except in very unusual circumstances a person should not change his religion. If a person was born to the Christian faith and lives in the Western world, then that person should keep the Christian faith because one absorbs religious beliefs as one absorbs the first sounds of one's language, and it often happens that if a person who is a Christian suddenly becomes a Hindu or a Buddhist, then certain hereditary factors, certain inbred conditions tend to weaken one's acceptance of the new faith, and all too often to compensate for that one will be avidly, fanatically in favor of the new religion, while at the same time having all sorts of unresolved doubts and conflicts beneath the surface. The result is rarely satisfactory. My own recommendation is that as a person is born, so he has accepted a religious belief, and thus he should keep to that belief."

"Mmmm!" I mused. "Then it seems that my ideas about religion have been all upside-down. It seems that one has to give and not ask for anything. One has to hope, instead, that someone will ask on one's behalf."

"One can ask for understanding, one can ask in prayer that one shall be able to assist others, because through assisting others one learns oneself, in teaching others one learns oneself, in saving others one saves oneself. One has to give before one can receive, one has to give of oneself, give of one's compassion, of one's mercy. Until one is able to give of oneself, one is not able to receive from others. One cannot obtain mercy without first showing mercy. One cannot obtain understanding without first having given understanding to the problems of others. Religion is a very big thing, Lobsang, too big to be dealt with in just one short talk like this. But think about it. Think what you can do for others, think how you can bring pleasure and spiritual advancement to others. And let me ask you something, Lobsang; you were instrumental in saving the life of a poor old monk who had an accident. If you face it squarely you will find that you derived pleasure and high satisfaction from that act. Is that not so?"

I thought about that, and yes, it was quite true, I had a lot of satisfaction from going down there after Honorable Puss Puss and then bringing help to the old man. "Yes, Honorable Master, you are correct, I had much satisfaction," I replied at last.

The evening shadows were falling, and the purple mantle of night was gradually spreading across our Valley. In far-off Lhasa the lights were beginning to twinkle and people were beginning to move behind their oil-silk screens. Somewhere below our window one of the cats gave a plaintive cry which was answered by another cat's voice from close at hand. My Guide stood up and stretched. He appeared to be stiff, and when I scrambled to my feet I nearly fell on my face because we had been sitting talking for longer than I thought, and yes—I was stiff too. Together we looked out of the window for a few moments, then my Guide said, "It might be a good idea to have a sound night's rest because—who knows?—we may be busy on the morrow. Good night to you, Lobsang, good night."

"Honorable Master," I said. "Thank you for the time and trouble you have taken explaining this to me. I am slow and I suppose sluggish in my mind, but I am beginning to get a little understanding. Thank you. Good night!"

I bowed to him and turned, and walked to the communicating door. "Lobsang," my Guide called to me. I turned and faced him. "The Lord Abbot really was pleased with you, and this is a matter which should go on record. The Lord Abbot is an austere, stern man. You have done well. Good night."

"Good night," I said again as I turned to my room. Quickly I made my very simple preparations for the night, and then I lay down—not to sleep immediately but to think of all the things which I had been told, and as I thought about it—yes—it was true, correct adherence to one's religion could provide most adequate and excellent spiritual discipline.

CHAPTER FOURTEEN

"Ow! Aaagh!!" Wearily I rolled over and lay for a few moments wondering where I was. Reluctantly I awoke, well—almost. The sky to the east was slightly pink. Ice crystals suspended high above in the up-draft from the mountain peaks glittered with prismatic flashes of rainbow hues. Right above me the heavens were still a deep purple, a purple which lightened even as I watched. My! It was cold. The stone floor was like a block of ice and I shivered. My old thin blanket was poor protection against my frigid bed. Yawning, I rubbed my knuckles into my eyes, trying to clear away the sleep, trying to put off for a few more minutes the effort of rising on this cold morning.

Irritably, still half asleep, I fumbled with my "pillow" which by day was my robe. Drugged with the effects of heavy sleep, I fumbled and poked, trying to find which way was "up" with my robe. In desperation—I could NOT awake properly—I made a wild guess and pulled the garment around me. With increasing crossness I discovered that I had it on inside out. Muttering to myself I tore it off. Literally "tore it off," for the rotten old thing split all the way down the back! Gloomily I surveyed the damage, standing naked in the frosty air, air so cold that my breath puffed out like a white cloud. Now I was in for it. What WOULD the Master of the Acolytes say? Damaging lamastic property—wanton carelessness—stupid numbskull of a boy—I knew ALL that he would say, he had said it to me so often.

We were not issued new robes. As a boy grew out of his robe he was given another which some other boy had outgrown. All our robes were old; some were held together more by faith than by strength. Now my robe was FINISHED, I concluded, as I looked at the sorry remains. Between my finger and thumb the fabric was thin, empty, devoid of "life." Sadly I sat down and pulled my blanket around me. WHAT SHOULD I DO NOW? Judiciously I made a few more rents and then, with my blanket wrapped round me like a robe, I went out in search of the Master of Acolytes. When I arrived at his office he was already saying truly horrid things to a small boy who wanted a different pair of sandals. "Feet were made before sandals, m'boy, feet were made before sandals!" he was saying. "If I had my way you would all go about barefoot, but—HERE— here is another pair. Take care of them. Well! What do YOU want?" he asked as he caught sight of me in my very threadbare blanket.

The way in which he looked at me! The way his eyes absolutely glared at the thought that another acolyte wanted something from his precious stores! "Honorable Master," I said with considerable trepidation, "my robe has split, but it is very, very thin and was long ago worn out."

"WORN OUT???" he bawled. "I am the one who says if a thing is worn out, not you, miserable boy. Now go about your business clad in rags for your audacity." One of the serving-monks bent forward and whispered something. The Master of the Acolytes scowled and bellowed, "What? What? Speak up, can't you, SPEAK UP!"

The serving-monk bawled back, "I said that this boy was recently sent for by the Inmost One. He was also sent for by my Lord Abbot here, and he is the chela of the Honorable Master Lama Mingyar Dondup."

"Ulp! Urragh!" gasped the Master of the Acolytes. "Why in the name of Buddha's Tooth didn't you tell me who he was? You are a dolt, an imbecile, worse than any of the acolytes!" The Master of the Acolytes turned to me with a synthetic smile upon his sharp features; I could see that it was causing him agony to look pleasant. He said, "Let me see the robe, my boy." Silently I passed him my robe with the back portion up so that the rents were the first thing he saw. He took the tattered garment, and very gently tugged at it. To my delight the tear increased, and with a final tug the garment was in two pieces. The Master of the Acolytes looked at me with openmouthed astonishment, and said, "Yes! It did tear easily, did it not? Come with me, my boy, you shall have a new robe." He put his hand on my elbow, and as he did so he felt my blanket. "Hmm! It is very threadbare; you must have been unfortunate with your blanket as with your robe. You shall have a new one." Together we went into some side room—well—room? It was more like a hall. Robes of all descriptions hung on hooks fixed to the wall, robes from those of high lamas down to the most menial type of garment for lay workers. Keeping my arm in his hand, he led me along with his lips pursed, and stopping every so often to feel a garment; it was as if he loved every one.

We came to the part where there were garments for acolytes. We stopped, and he fingered his chin and then tugged at the lobes of his ears. "So you are the boy who was first blown down the mountain and was then blown up to the Golden Roof? Hmmm! And you are the boy who went and saw the Inmost One by special command, eh? Hmmm! And you are the boy whom I personally heard talking to the Lord Abbot of this Lamasery? Hmmm! And you—well, well, that's most extraordinary—you have gained the favor of the Lord Abbot himself. Hmmm!" He frowned and appeared to be looking into the far distance. My guess was that he was trying to decide if I would have to see the Inmost One again or if I would have to see the Lord Abbot again, and—who knows?—even a small boy can be used to further the aims of an ambitious man.

"I am going to do something very unusual. I am going to give you a completely new robe, one that was made only last week. If the Inmost One has favored you, and the Lord Abbot has favored you, and the great Lama Mingyar Dondup has favored you, then I must see that you are dressed so that you can go into their presences without bringing shame to me. Hmmm!" He turned away and led the way to yet another room, an annex off the big store. Here there were new robes which had just been made by monks working under the direction of lamas. He fingered a pile which had not yet been hung up on the racks, and taking out one he said, "Put it on, let us try it for fit." Quickly I discarded my blanket, being careful to fold it neatly, and then tried on this brand-new robe. As I well knew, if one had a brand-new robe it was a sign to the other acolytes, and to monks as well, that one had "pull" somewhere and so was a person of some consequence. So I was glad indeed to have a new robe because, while an old robe was sometimes taken as an indication that one had been an acolyte for a long time, a brand-new robe was the sign-manual that one was important.

The new robe fitted me well. It was much thicker and even the few moments it had been on me had brought a warm glow to my formerly shivering body. "This fits perfectly, Master," I said with some pleasure.

"Hmmm! I think we may do a little better than that. Wait a moment." He dug down into the pile, mumbling and muttering, and every so often fingering his beads. At last he moved aside to another pile, and took out a far better quality garment. With a sigh, he fairly groaned, "This is one of a special batch, they were made by accident from a superior material. Now try this on, I think it will make quite an impression on our seniors."

Yes, there was no doubt about it. It was a fine robe. It fitted me well, rather long perhaps, coming right down to my feet, but that meant that I would have room to grow, and this brand-new robe would last me longer. Anyway, a thing that was a bit too big could always be shortened by having a bigger "bay" in front and with a bigger pouch in front I could carry more things around with me. I turned around and around, and the Master of the Acolytes looked carefully at me, and then at last he nodded his head and pulled at his bottom lip before remarking with considerable gloom, "Having gone so far, we must surely go a little farther. You shall have that robe, my boy, and I will give you another, because I perceive that you are one who has no spare robe." I found it difficult to follow what he was saying because he was mumbling away with his back turned to me, digging into the pile of robes. At last he came up with another one, saying, "Now try this on to see if this, also, fits you. I know that you are the boy who has been given a special room in the Lamas' Quarters, so your robe will not be taken from you by some bigger boy."

I was delighted. Now I had two robes, one for spare and one for everyday use. The Master of the Acolytes looked with considerable distaste at my blanket, and remarked, "Oh, yes, we were going to give you a new blanket. Come with me and bring that one with you." He hastened ahead of me out into the main storage hall and called for a monk, who came bringing a ladder with him. Quickly the monk went up the ladder and took then from some shelves a blanket. It contrasted rather too much with my robe, so, with a groan of sheer anguish, the Master of the Acolytes took the steps himself and went back into the side room, returning after a few moments with his eyes half closed and with a superior quality blanket. "Take it, my boy, take it," he quavered. "This is one of our better blankets made by accident from superior stock. Take it, and remember, when you see the Lord Abbot or the Inmost One that I have treated you well and outfitted you grandly." In all seriousness I tell you that the Master of the Acolytes cupped his hands over his eyes while he groaned at the thought of parting with his better quality materials.

"I am much indebted to you, Honorable Master," was my reply. "I am sure" (here my diplomacy came into play!) "that my Master, the Lama Mingyar Dondup, will very speedily perceive your goodness in giving me these garments. Thank you!" With that off my chest I turned and made my way out of the storeroom.

As I did so one of the serving-monks outside solemnly winked at me, and I had much difficulty in not laughing out loud.

Back I went, up the corridor and into the enclosure of the Lamas' Quarters. As I was hastening along with a robe and a blanket in my arms I almost bumped into my Guide. "Oh, Honorable Master!" I exclaimed. "I am so sorry, but I could not see you."

My Guide laughed at me saying, "You look like a travelling salesman, Lobsang, you look as if you have just come back over the mountains from India. Have you set up as a trader by any chance?" I told him about my misfortunes, told him how my robe had split all the way down. I told him, too, that the Master of the Acolytes had been telling a boy that he would have all boys go barefoot. My Guide led the way into his room and we sat down. Immediately my interior gave notice that I had had no food and fortunately for me my Guide heard that warning, and he smiled as he said, "So you, too, have not yet broken your fast? Then let us break our fast together." With that he reached out his hand and rang his little silver bell.

With tsampa before us, we made no remarks until we had finished our meal. Later, when the monk had cleared away the dishes, my Guide said, "So you have made an impression on the Master of the Acolytes? You must have made a sound impression to get two good robes and a new blanket. I shall have to see if I can emulate you!"

"Master, I am very curious about clothing, for if the Master of the Acolytes says that we should all go about without sandals, then why should we not go about without clothes?"

My Guide laughed at me and remarked, "Many years ago, of course, people did not wear clothes, and because they did not wear clothes they did not feel the lack of such garments, because in those days people were able to have their bodies compensate for a much wider range of temperatures. But now, through using clothing, we have become effete, and we have ruined our heat-regulating mechanisms by abusing them." He fell silent, musing over the problem. Then he laughed as he continued, "But can you imagine some of the fat old monks around here going about with nothing on? It would be quite a sight! But the story of clothes is a very interesting one because in the first case people wore no clothing at all, and thus there was no treachery because each person could see the aura of others. But at last the leaders of the tribes of those days decided that they needed something to distinguish them as leaders so they would use a bunch of feathers strategically placed, or a few coats of paint made from various berries But then the ladies came into the picture; they wanted to be decorated also, and they used bunches of leaves even more strategically placed." My Guide laughed at the thought of all these people, and I could conjure up quite a good picture myself.

He continued, "When the head man and the head woman of each tribe had themselves all decorated, then the next in line of succession had to have some decoration also, and thus they became indistinguishable from the head man and the head woman, so the head man and the head woman had to add even more decorations, and so the matter went on for quite a time, each leading man adding more clothing. Eventually the leading women wore clothing which was definitely suggestive, clothing intended to half reveal that which should not be concealed, for—do not misunderstand me—when people could see the aura, then there could be no treachery, no wars, no double-dealings. It was only since people started wearing clothing that they ceased to be able to see the aura, and they ceased to be clairvoyant and telepathic." He looked hard at me and said, "Now you pay attention to me, because this has much bearing on the task which you will have to do later." I nodded to show that I really was paying attention.

My Guide continued, "A clairvoyant who can see the astral of another has to be able to see the unclad body if he is to be able to give a quite accurate reading of any illness, and when people wear clothing their aura becomes contaminated." I sat up in some astonishment at that because I did not see how clothing could contaminate an aura, and I said so. My Guide soon answered me: "A person is naked, so the aura from that person is the aura of that person and not of anything else. Now, if you put a yak-wool garment on the person, you take in the aural influence of the yak, the person who sheared the yak, the person who combed and carded the wool, and the person who actually wove the material. So, if you are going to bother about the aura seen through clothing, you may be able to tell of the intimate history of the yak and its family, which is not at all what you want."

"But, Master," was my anxious question, "how does clothing contaminate an aura?"

"Well, I've just told you; everything that exists has its own field of influence, its own magnetic field, and if you take a view through that window you can see the bright daylight, but if you pull our oil silk screens across you see the bright daylight which is now modified by the influence of the oil-silk screens. In other words, what you actually see is a bluish tinge to the light, and that would not at all help you in describing what sunlight was like."

He smiled rather wryly at me as he continued, "It is rather remarkable, really, that people are so unwilling to part with their clothing. I always have had the theory that people have a racial memory that without clothing their aura could be seen and read by others, and so many people nowadays have such guilty thoughts that they dare not let anyone else know what is on their mind and so they keep clothing on their body, which is a sign of guilt masquerading under the misnomer of purity and innocence." He reflected for a few moments, then remarked, "Many religions say that Man is made in the image of God, but then Man is ashamed of his body, which seems to imply that Man is ashamed of the image of God. It is all very puzzling how people go on. You will find in the West that people show surprising amounts of flesh in certain areas, but they cover other areas so that attention is automatically drawn to it. In other words, Lobsang, many women wear clothing which is completely suggestive; they wear padded portions which were also known as 'gay deceivers' when I was in the West. All these pads are designed to make a man think a woman has that which she has not, in the same way as just a few years ago men of the West wore things inside their trousers which they called 'cod pieces.' That is, there were certain pads of material which were meant to convey the impression that a man was generously endowed and thus would be a very virile partner. Unfortunately, the ones with the most padding were the least virile! But another great difficulty with clothing is that it keeps out fresh air. If people would wear less clothing, and would have air baths, their health would greatly improve; there would be less cancer, and very much less tuberculosis, because when a person is all swaddled up with clothing, air cannot circulate and germs multiply."

I thought about that, and I just did not see for one moment how germs would multiply if a person wore clothes, and I expressed that view. My Guide responded: "Lobsang! If you look about on the ground you may not see many insects about, but if you lift a rotten log or move a big stone, you will find all sorts of things beneath. Insects, worms, and various types of creatures which breed and live only in dark and secluded places are there. In the same way, the body is covered with bacteria, covered with germs. The action of light prevents the germs and the bacteria from multiplying, it has an effect of keeping the body healthy. But as soon as one allows pockets of stagnant air to rest in the darkness of thick clothing one gets all sorts of bacteria multiplying." He looked at me quite seriously as he said, "Later when you are a doctor treating patients, you will find that if a dressing is left too long untended, maggots will form beneath in just the same way as when a stone is left on the ground insects will collect beneath it. But that is a thing you will deal with in the future."

He rose to his feet, and stretched and said, "But now we have to go out. I think I will give you five minutes to get ready, and then go down to the stables because we are going on a journey together." With that he motioned for me to pick up my spare robe and my blanket and take them to my own room. I bowed to him, and gathered my bundle and turned through the communicating door. For a few moments I was busy getting myself ready, and then I made my way down to the stables as directed.

As I went out into the open of the courtyard I stopped in amazement; there was quite a cavalcade being assembled. For some moments I hung around against one of the walls, moving from foot to foot as I wondered who all this was for. For a moment I thought one of the abbots was getting ready to move, but then my Guide, the Lama Mingyar Dondup, appeared and looked rapidly around. Seeing me he beckoned. My heart sank as I realized that all this commotion was for us.

There was a horse for my Guide and a smaller horse for me. In addition, there were four monk-attendants each mounted on a horse, and as well as that there were four more horses laden with bundles and packages, but laden in such a way that they were not carrying too much weight so that two of them could at any time be used as spares in order that the heavier men would not overtire their own horses. There was much heavy breathing through nostrils, the stamping of feet, and the swishing of tails, and I walked forward exerting the greatest care not to get behind any horse for, once before, a playful horse had lured me behind him, and then he had planted a hoof with considerable force in the middle of my chest, knocking me over and actually cartwheeling me on the ground. Since then I had exercised care.

"Well, we are going up into the mountains, Lobsang, for two or three days, and you are going as my assistant!" His eyes twinkled as he said that, actually it was another stage in my training. Together we walked to our horses, and the one allotted to me turned his head and really shuddered as he recognized me; his eyes rolled and he neighed in bitter protest. My sympathy was entirely with him, because I did not like him any more than he liked me, but—a monk-groom quickly extended his cupped hands and helped me onto my horse. My Guide was already mounted on his and was waiting. The monk-groom whispered, "This is a quiet horse, you shouldn't have any trouble with this one—not even you!"

My Guide looked around him, checking that I was just behind him, and that the four monk-attendants were also in position, and the four pack-horses were attached by long tethers. Then he raised his hand and we rode off down the mountain. Horses allotted to me seemed to have one thing in common, whenever there was a particularly steep piece the wretched beast would put his head down and I had to cling on to prevent myself from sliding over his neck. This time I braced my feet behind his ears—he liked that no more than I liked his head being down! The terraced road was jerky, there was much traffic, and I had all my abilities concentrated on staying on my horse. But I did manage as we rounded a bend once to glance up and out across the park-land to that which had once been my home and was now my home no longer.

Down we went, down the mountain and turned left into the Linghor Road. We plodded on over the river bridge and as we came in sight of the Chinese Mission we suddenly turned right on the road which led to the Kashya Linga, and I wondered why such an entourage would be going just to that little park. My Guide had given me no indication of where we were going to "the mountains," and as there were mountains all around Lhasa enclosing us in a sort of bowl, that was no guide at all to our destination.

Suddenly I jumped for joy, so suddenly that my wretched horse started to buck, thinking that I was attacking him or something. However, I managed to hang on and pulled the reins so tight that his head came right back; that soon made him quiet and so I had learned a lesson—keep a tight rein and your seat is safe, I hoped! We went on at a steady walk and soon reached a widening of the road where there were a number of traders just disembarking from the ferries. My Guide dismounted and his senior monk-attendant dismounted also and strode over to the ferryman. For a few moments there was conversation, then the monk came back, saying, "It is all right, Honorable Lama, we go now." Immediately there was bustle and confusion. The monk-attendants got off their horses and all converged on the pack-horses. The loads were removed and carried into the boat of the ferryman. Then all the horses were tied together with long leads, and two attendant-monks each mounted a horse and walked it into the river. I watched as they started out, the monks pulling their robes right up around them, right up beyond their waists, and the horses all bravely plunging into the water and swimming away across to the other side. My Guide, I saw with some astonishment, was already in the boat and motioning me to enter also. So for the first time in my life I clambered aboard a boat, to be followed by the two other attendants. With a muttered word to his assistant, the ferryman pushed off. For a moment there was a sensation of giddiness because the boat spun around in a circle.

This boat was made of the skins of yaks, carefully stitched together and made waterproof. Then the thing was inflated with air. People with their goods got in and the boatman just took long sweeps, or oars, and paddled slowly across the river. Whenever there was a wind against him, he took a long, long time, but he always made up for it on the return journey because then it was just a question of guiding and the wind blowing.

I was too excited to know much about that first trip across the water. I know that I clutched the sides of the skin-boat so there was some danger of my fingers, with sharp nails, penetrating. I was, in any case, afraid to move because every time I tried to move something sagged beneath me. It was almost as if we were resting on nothingness, and it was not at all like resting upon a good solid stone floor which did not rock. In addition, the water was rather choppy and I came to the conclusion that I had eaten too much, for curious qualms assailed me in the stomach and I was very frightened that I would be heartily sick in front of all those men. However, by holding my breath at judicious intervals, I managed to preserve my honor, and soon the boat grated on a shallow pebbly beach, and we alighted.

Our cavalcade reassembled, my Guide in the lead and I half a horse-length behind him, then the four monk-attendants riding two and two, and after that the four pack-horses. My Guide looked about to make sure that everyone was ready, and then his horse stepped forward toward the morning.

We sat and sat, while our horses jogged on and on. All the time we were facing the west, the direction in which the morning had gone, for we say that the sun rises in the east and travels west taking the morning with it. Soon the sun overtook us and was dead overhead. There was no cloud, and the rays of the sun were scorching indeed, but when we came into the shadow of great rocks the cold was bitter because at our altitude there was insufficient air to balance out the hot rays of the sun and the coldness of the shadows. We rode on for perhaps another hour, and then my Guide came to a part of the trail which apparently he used as a stopping place. Without any signals that I could perceive, the monks got off their horses and immediately started to boil water, taking dried yak dung which we used as fuel, and going to a nearby mountain stream for water. In about half an hour we were sitting down having our tsampa, and I for one certainly felt the need of it. The horses also were fed, and then they were all taken off to the mountain stream so that they could be watered.

I sat with my back against a boulder, a boulder which looked to be about as big as the buildings of Chakpori Temple. I looked out from our high position across the Valley of Lhasa; the air was absolutely clear, no haze, no dust, and we could see everything with utter clarity. We could see pilgrims going by the Western Gate, we could see the traders, and we could look far back down the trail and see the boatman bringing yet another load of passengers across the Happy River.

Soon it was time to move on, so the horses were again loaded and we all mounted, and then rode along up the mountain path, going deeper and deeper into the foothills of the Himalayas. Soon we abandoned the established road which eventually led into India, and we turned left where the road—rather a track this time—became steeper and steeper, and where our progress became much, much slower. Above us, perched on a ledge, we could see a small lamasery. I looked at it with great interest because it was a source of fascination for me, it was a lamasery of a slightly different Order, an Order in which the monks and lamas were all married and they lived in the building with their families.

We went on and on, hour after hour, and soon drew level with this lamasery of a different Order. We could see monks and nuns walking about together, and I was quite surprised to see that the nuns also had shaved heads. Here they had dark faces, faces which glistened, and then my Guide whispered to me, "Here there are many sand storms, so they all wear a thick mask of grease which preserves the skin. Later we, too, shall have to put on leather facemasks."

It was a fortunate thing that my horse was surefooted and knew more about mountain trails than I did, because my attention was completely on that small lamasery. I could see small children playing about, and it really puzzled me why there should be some monks who lived a celibate life and others who got married, and I wondered why it should make such a break between two branches of the same religion. The monks and nuns just looked up at our passing, and then took no more notice of us, took less notice of us than if we had been traders.

We climbed on and on, and above us we saw a white and ocher building perched on what I should have called a wholly inaccessible ledge of rock. My Guide pointed it out, "That is where we are going,

Lobsang, up to that hermitage. We have to get up there tomorrow morning because the way is dangerous indeed; tonight we shall sleep here among the rocks."

We rode on for, perhaps, another mile, and then we stopped amid a cluster of rocks, great rocks, which formed almost a saucer. We rode the horses in among the rocks and then we all dismounted. The horses were tethered and fed; we had our tsampa, and then—night was upon us like the drawing of a curtain. I rolled myself in my blanket and peered out between two rocks. I could see various glimmers of light from Chakpori and from the Potala, the moon was shining very brightly and the Happy River might well have been named the Silver River for it was shining as a streak of purest, bright silver. The night was still, no breath of wind, no movement, not even a night bird called. The stars were gleaming bright in their myriad hues above. On the instant I fell asleep.

I had a good night's rest with no interruptions for temple services, no interruptions for anything, but in the morning when I awoke I felt as though I had been trampled by a herd of yaks. Every bone ached and I felt I would not be able to sit down with any degree of comfort, then I remembered that wretched horse and I hoped he ached as well, although I had grave doubts about that. Soon our little camp was a-bustle with serving-monks who were preparing tsampa. I wandered away while they were doing so and stood gazing out across the Valley of Lhasa. Then I turned and looked up at the hermitage some quarter of a mile above. It looked a strange place, it reminded me of one of those bird's nests which are stuck tight against the wall of a house, and which one always expects to fall and shatter at any moment. I could not see any path or any way at all of reaching the hermitage.

I wandered back and had my tsampa, and listened to the men talk. Soon—as soon as we had finished our breakfast—my Guide said, "Well, we shall have to be moving, Lobsang. The horses and three of the monk-attendants remain here, we and one of the attendants move up." My heart sank at the thought of that, how

190

was I going to walk all the way up the mountain side? I was sure that if the horses could not travel that way I could not either. However, ropes were obtained from one of the horses and draped around the monk-attendant. Then I carried one bag of I know not what, and my Guide took another, while the rather bulky monk-attendant took the third. The three monks left behind looked very happy that they were going to have some time alone without any supervision, without anything to do except look after the horses. We set out, and plodded up between the rocks finding a precarious foothold when we could. Soon the way became worse and worse, and the monk-attendant took the lead, throwing a rope with two stones attached to the end. He would throw, make a quick jerk, and the stones would swing around and trap the rope, and then he would pull to see if it was straight. After which he would pull himself up with the rope, then, reaching the end, he would steady it so that my Guide and I could make our slow dangerous way. The process was repeated time after time.

Eventually, after one particularly arduous effort, we reached a platform of rock, a platform that was perhaps thirty feet wide and had obviously been carved out by some age-old avalanche. As I thankfully reached it and pulled myself over the edge, climbing first to my knees and then to my feet, I turned my gaze to the right and there several feet away was the hermitage.

For some moments we stood there, all of us panting while we got our breath back. I was enthralled with the view; I could look down upon the Golden Roof of the Potala, I could look also into the courtyards of the Chakpori. I could see that obviously a fresh load of herbs had just arrived, for the place was like a disturbed beehive, monks were scurrying in all directions. There was much traffic, too, through the Western Gate. But then I sighed, this was not for me, I had, instead, to go climbing silly mountains and go to meet people in hermitages when who but an idiot would live walled up in a hermitage?

Now there were signs of activity, because from the hermitage three men approached. One was very, very old and was being supported by two younger men. As they came toward us, we picked up our baggage again and advanced to the hermitage.

CHAPTER FIFTEEN

THE OLD MAN was blind—totally blind. I looked at his eyes with wonder, they were PECULIAR. For some time I could not place what it was that made me think they were so strange, and then I heard how he had been blinded.

In Tibet hermits are immured in cells deep within a hermitage. The cells are completely and utterly without light, and after three to seven years, if a man wants to be let out, if he feels that his self-imposed withdrawal should end, then it takes a considerable time. First a very small hole is made in the roof so that a minute trace of light can then enter. After several days the hole is made larger so that after perhaps a month the man inside is able to see again, because during his incarceration the pupils of the eye open fully and if light should suddenly enter the man would instantly be struck blind. This old man had been in a cell, one side of which had been hit by a falling rock, tearing it off. At one moment the hermit had been sitting in the cell where he had sat for some twenty years; the next thing was a terrific crash and rumble, and the side of his hermitage had been torn away, and the old man was looking directly into the face of the burning sun. Instantly he had been struck blind.

I listened to what the old man was telling my Guide: "So in accordance with custom we provided the food on the first day, and on the second day, and on the third day, but the food was untouched, and thus as our Brother does not answer we believe that his soul has taken wing away from the empty shell of the body."

My Guide took the old man by the arm, saying, "Do

not be disturbed, my Brother, for we will look into the matter. Perhaps you will lead us to the cell?"

The others turned and led the way into and across their small courtyard. To the left there was a series of small cells, five cells I observed, very bare, very barren of comforts, for they were just cells, just stone caves in the rocky side of the mountain. No tables, no tankas, nothing; just a stone floor upon which a monk could sit or lie in sleep. We passed those and we entered a large dark room, a room which was perched precariously on a rocky spur jutting out from the side of the mountain. It looked a shaky contraption to me, but apparently it had survived there for a couple of hundred years.

In the center of this large gloomy room was another room. As we went into it the darkness increased. Butter lamps were brought, and we entered a small corridor, which was pitch-black; about ten paces and we came up against a blank wall. The butter lamps shed a feeble glow which seemed to accentuate the darkness. My Guide took one of the lamps and held it just about at chest-level, and then I saw there was a very closely fitting trap door. My Guide opened it and felt about in what appeared to be a cupboard. Loudly he rapped on the inner side of the cupboard and listened carefully. Then he put his lamp inside, and I saw that it was apparently a box let into the wall. My Guide said, "This is a box, Lobsang, with two doors, this door and a door inside. The occupant of the cell waits until a certain time, then he opens his door, feels about and removes food and water placed for him. He never sees light, he never speaks to anyone, he is, in fact, under a vow of silence. Now we have the problem that he has been without food for several days, and we do not know if he is alive or dead."

He looked at the opening, then he looked at me. Looking back to the opening he measured it with his hand and arm then he measured me, after which he said, "It seems to me that if you took off your robe you could just possibly scrape through this opening and force open the door on the other side, then you could see if the monk was in need of attention."

194

"Ow! Master!" I exclaimed in complete fright. "What happens if I go through and can't get out?"

My Guide thought for a moment, and then answered, "First you shall be lifted up so that you are supported. Then you can, with a stone, batter in the inner door. When you have battered it in we will slide you in and you can hold a lamp in your outstretched hands. It should be bright enough to permit you to see if the man is in need of help."

My Guide went into the other room and took three butter lamps, prying the wicks out of two of them, and putting the three together twisted into one lamp which he very carefully packed with butter. In the meantime one of the monks had gone out into the open, and he now returned carrying quite a substantial rock. He handed it to me and I hefted it for weight and balance. "Master, why cannot the monk answer a question?" I asked.

"Because he is under oath, under a vow not to speak for a certain time," was the response.

I reluctantly shed my robe, shivering in the cold mountain air. Chakpori was cold enough, but here it was colder still, the chill was biting. I kept on my sandals because the floor was like a block of ice.

In the meantime a monk had taken the stone and had given a good bonk against the inner door, which sprang out of its frame with a loud crash, but the others, although they tried hard, were not able to see into the inner cell. Their heads were too big, their shoulders were too wide. So my Guide held me horizontally and I extended my hands as if I was going to dive, and one of the monks lit the three wicks now fixed in the butter lamp putting it carefully between my hands. Then I was slid forward. I found the frame of the wretched cupboard, or passage, very rough, but with many a grunt and exclamation I was eased into the box-like entrance, being twisted sideways and joggled to and fro so that at last my arms and my head protruded. Immediately I was overcome by a sickening stench. It was absolutely foul, it was the smell of rotting meat, the smell of things gone bad. One smelled

195

something comparable when one chanced upon a dead yak or a dead horse which had been kept too long; it was a smell which reminded me of all the sanitary appliances in the world, having gone wrong at the same time! I was absolutely gagging with the stench, but I managed to control myself enough to hold the light aloft, and in its flickering gleams reflected from the stone walls I could see the old monk. His eyes were shining at me, he was staring at me, and I jumped so much with fright that I scraped a whole lot of skin off my shoulders. I gazed back at him, and then I saw that his eyes were shining in the reflected light but they did not blink, they did not waver. I waggled my feet as a signal that I wanted to be out—in a hurry. Gently I was pulled back, and then I was sick, sick, sick!

"We cannot leave him there!" said my Guide. "We shall have to knock the wall down and get him out." I recovered from my nausea and put on my robe. The others got tools consisting of a heavy hammer and two iron bars with flattened ends. Then they applied the iron bars to niches in a far part of the wall, and hammered. Gradually a block was removed, and then another, and another. The stench was terrible. At last the opening was big enough for a man to enter, and one of the monks entered bearing two butter lamps. Soon he returned looking grey-faced and he repeated my performance, which I was glad to note.

"We shall have to put a rope around him and drag him out," said that monk, "he is falling to pieces. He is very much in a state of decay." Silently a monk left the room and shortly returned with a long length of rope. Entering the hole in the wall (where the door had originally been walled-up) we heard him moving about, and then he returned. "It is all right, you can pull," he said. Two monks gently took the rope and pulled. Soon the old man's head appeared, and his arms; he was in a terrible state. The monks carefully pulled him out and then he was lifted up by tender hands and borne outside.

At the far side of the room there was a small trail

leading farther up the mountain. The two monks with their burden ascended the path and disappeared out of our sight. I knew that they were going to take the body to a flat surface where the vultures would soon devour it, because there was no chance of burying bodies here in the hard mountain rocks, we depended upon "air burial."

While this was being done the monk-attendant who was with us had made a small hole in the far side of the wall that let in a dull gleam of light. Then he took pails of water and swilled down the inner cell, cleaning it from its last occupant. Soon—how soon—there would be someone else taking over that cell and would live there for ten? twenty? how many years?

Later that day we were all sitting down and the old blind man said, "I can feel that here we have one who is destined to travel far and to see much. I have received information about him from when my hands touched his head. Boy, sit before me."

Reluctantly I moved forward and sat right in front of the old blind man. He lifted his hands—they were as cold as ice—and placed them upon my shaven skull. His fingers lightly traced the outline of my head and probed various bumps I had. Then he spoke: "You are going to have a very hard life." I groaned to myself. Everyone was telling me I was going to have a hard life and I was getting heartily sick of the whole affair. "After you have had hardships, trials, and tribulations that fall to few, you will just before the end have success. You will do that for which you came to this world."

I had heard it all before. I had been to soothsayers, seers, astrologers, and clairvoyants, and every one of them had told me the same type of thing. After having told me that he just waved his hands, so I got up and moved as far away as I could, an act which caused him to cackle with amusement.

My Guide and the others were in a long discussion of very serious matters. It did not make much sense to me, they were talking about prophecies and things that were going to happen in Tibet, they were telling about the best methods of preserving the Sacred Knowledge, and how already steps were being made to take various books and articles high up into the mountains where they would be hidden in caves. They were saying, too, how counterfeit things were going to be left in the temples so that the old, old genuine articles would not fall into the hands of the invader of later years.

I moved out of the enclosure and sat on a rock, gazing out where far below the City of Lhasa was now hidden by the gloom of the fast approaching night. Only the higher peaks of Chakpori and the Potala were still in the faint dusk light. They appeared to be two islands floating upon a sea of the deepest purple. As I sat there gradually the islands appeared to be submerged in the all-pervading darkness. Then as I sat, a bright shaft of moonlight striking down over the mountain edge touched the roof of the Potala which was lighted with golden gleams. I turned and walked inside the enclosure where I took off my robe, rolled myself in my blanket, and fell asleep.

the world at large, Doc Savage is a strange, mysterious figure
glistening bronze skin and golden eyes. To his fans he is the
eatest adventure hero of all time, whose fantastic exploits are
equaled for hair-raising thrills, breathtaking escapes, blood-
rdling excitement!

- ☐ S7102   HAUNTED OCEAN (75¢)
- ☐ S7519   THE MAN OF BRONZE (75¢)
- ☐ S7520   THE THOUSAND HEADED MAN (75¢)
- ☐ S7521   METEOR MENACE (75¢)
- ☐ S7522   THE POLAR TREASURE (75¢)
- ☐ S7524   THE LOST OASIS (75¢)
- ☐ S5788   THE MUNITIONS MASTER (75¢)
- ☐ S6653   THE MOTION MENACE (75¢)
- ☐ S6725   THE GREEN DEATH (75¢)
- ☐ S6923   THE FRECKLED SHARK (75¢)
- ☐ S5947   THE LIVING FIRE MENACE (75¢)
- ☐ S6542   THE SUBMARINE MYSTERY (75¢)
- ☐ S5838   THE YELLOW CLOUD (75¢)